400/414

ATOMS AND PEOPLE

Ralph E. Lapp

ATOMS AND PEOPLE

HARPER

&

BROTHERS,

PUBLISHERS,

NEW

YORK

CONTENTS

AUTHOR'S NOTE

Half of my life has been spent studying atoms. At first, I concentrated on purely scientific aspects in a normal manner, doing research for my doctorate. This orderly process was rudely disrupted by two dissimilar events, Pearl Harbor and the splitting of the uranium atom, which seemed to have little connection at the time but which later came full circle with the A-bomb and Hiroshima.

With the end of the war and release from preoccupation with a military harness for the atom, I was free again to return to the calm absorption of the research laboratory. But I was troubled by a gnawing uneasiness. The atom, it seemed to me, although I felt this rather vaguely, was more than science and technology. It was a rearing, titanic force released upon an unsuspecting and ill-conditioned planet. Moreover, it was a puny and primitive forerunner of cataclysmic forces yet to be spawned. These forces would remake man's way of life, for good or evil, depending upon his wisdom or his folly.

I decided to wander outside the ivory tower and have a look at the extent to which the atom would remake the world. In effect, I decided to study atoms and people rather than just the former. By that I mean the impact of this new force upon our society. The first, most important thing to learn about was the military application of atomic energy, so I accepted a position with the Defense Department and spent some three years in the mammoth Pentagon along the banks of the Potomac.

Having arrived at the ripe old age of thirty, I took stock of my meandering career, which had gone off its beeline flight into the Elysian fields of pure science. Two excursions, a wartime detour into technology and a postwar interlude with the military atom, gave me new perspectives but showed me no pastures greener than those of basic science. I decided to leave the Defense Department and brush up on science by writing a textbook on nuclear physics. Writing proved infectious once I disciplined myself to the rigors of translating thoughts to the printed word. I wrote another book, this time about the atom and national defense, and it soon became obvious that I was rapidly becoming immersed in politics. The atom, infinitesimal in size, had become a political football, and I could scarcely write about it without involving both politics and personalities. I found myself spending more and more time on Capitol Hill, attending Congressional hearings.

My eyes popped wide open at what I found on Capitol Hill. In the Pentagon, one had to tiptoe in very strictly prescribed manner and gain formal access to specific secret areas on a "need to know" basis. I must confess that at the time this privileged view of secret data gave me a rather smug attitude toward those "on the outside." Yet, when I got on the outside, and particularly on the Hill, I discovered that almost everything was out in the open. Moreover, I no longer had to justify in advance why I needed to know something. I began to perceive that the strict compartmentalization of data into secret cubicles in the various government agencies was largely self-defeating, for it isolated people from vital data so that they could not see broader issues.

It's been eight years since I have seen a paper stamped "Atomic Energy Restricted Data" or "Secret"; yet, I feel very confident that this is not a handicap but is in fact a very real advantage. I can write freely and draw upon open information sources. Furthermore, since I am completely independent, I do not have to submit my manuscripts to a supervisor for approval—a process which would sharply restrict any critical view of atomic energy. In reviewing what I have written in this book, I am quite certain that were I employed by the Atomic Energy Commission, I would be in a most uncomfortable position. During the last several years I have witnessed an alarming tendency for scientists within the AEC either to say nothing or to follow a party line. If the scientists cannot speak out on the great issues of our day, then the fundamental processes of democracy will be interdicted. And if scientists follow a party line, dictated by political factors, how long will it be before science, itself, is corrupted? This is a frightening prospect but it is not a chimeric one.

All of this foregoing description may explain, in part, how I came to write this book about atomic energy. But I must confess that I could not have translated the technology of the atom into easily understood terms had it not been for some additional experience during the past three years. I have busied myself with lectures from one end of the country to the other, explaining the atom and what it means to everyone. My first public appearances must have been sorry shows for I was aghast at the idea of mounting the lecture platform; it was about the last place in the world I expected to find myself. But the power of the atom was so great that it propelled me onto the platform. Gradually, by answering questions after talks and by close association with such varied audiences as women's clubs, men's forums, university convocations and professional groups, I hit upon the level which would neither go over the head of the listener nor insult his intelligence. My impression is that all too often people are credited with mental deficiency, and I was encouraged to discover a high degree of understanding.

In meeting with people from all walks of life, I have been rather astonished to find that their concept of the scientist is that of an austere automaton. In fact, very much like the picture painted by one of Sinclair Lewis' characters in *Arrowsmith* when at a cocktail party, she buttonholed Dr. Arrowsmith and exclaimed, "The trouble with scientists is that they do not understand beauty. They are so cold." Scientists are no different from plumbers, or farmers, or ironworkers. They are flesh and blood and have the same aspirations, but they appear to stand off from society because of their alien world and strange, almost foreign language. The infinitesimal dimension of the atom, the world-shaking forces engaged there and the passionate dedication of the scientist to his work all combine to make the nuclear scientist a man apart. This apparent ostracism does not, however, isolate the scientist from beauty. Probing into the interstices of the atom, the physicist glimpses the rare beauty of nature's exquisite watchwork design, the harmony of which surpasses the lay imagination.

The layman readily appreciates the beauty of breath-taking flowers or a spectacular sunset and some even perceive the grandeur of scaling a mountain peak, but so few possess the vision to sense the unseen beauty of our miniature atomic universe, the nature of which we are just beginning to understand and the impact of which has changed and will continue to alter man's place on this planet.

Scientists in quest of pure knowledge have stumbled upon the keys to unlock the doors of a new world. Dazed and blinking in the dazzling light, they have groped their way over untrod paths, seeking to discover even more. But what they have already found confounds humanity with the predicament of a split world and a split atom. Some of us, and I judge the number to be small, have been frightened, especially when the doors of hell parted briefly at Hiroshima and Nagasaki. We have stammered out fears and warned of the Stygian perils which lurk in the vortical nuclear maelstrom in which the world is caught. We have attempted to bridge the gap between the scientist and the layman.

We know not whether the atom will bring the long-sought blessing of permanent peace or convulse whole nations in its savage grip. But the promise of atomic energy is so bright that we may even now regard it as the great revolutionary force of our century, man's crowning accomplishment since his first use of fire. I hope that in the pages which follow, I have imparted some sense of the nobility of this accomplishment, the dim outlines of which we barely discern but which we know will be the basis of a new mode of life for generations to come.

R. E. LAPP

May 21, 1956
Arlington, Virginia

ATOMS AND PEOPLE

chapter 1

THE ATOM IS SPLIT

Back in 1938 I started to study nuclear physics. Torn between two loves, science and literature, I could not make up my mind which field to choose. I tarried an extra year in high school, worrying over the decision, pondering the future or, more importantly, my future. Even then I could not resolve the dilemma, so I groped my way through a year at college with one foot planted on the solid ground of science and the other on the less firm terrain of literature.

Trauma induced decision. A nasty infection invaded the delicate tissues of my brain, and a wonderful Italian surgeon followed suit. After chopping through the abnormally thick bone of my head, he found a very confused state of affairs with some essential equipment quite out of place. As he later remarked, on informing me that I had a coin-flipping chance to survive, "Everything was all mixed up in there."

I do not know what the doctor did to me; all I know is that when I regained consciousness, my decision was made: I wanted to become a nuclear scientist. It was as simple as that, but I suppose that psychologists have quite a complicated explanation for this type of decision-making.

My mind made up, I proceeded on a straight-line course to my goal, never once deviating although with many a backward glance at my abandoned pursuit of writing. I absorbed myself in studies on the campus of the University of Chicago, which was to be my world for the next seven years. Shut in by the gray Gothic architecture, I felt only a slight rumble of events in Europe.

That fateful year of 1938 focused attention upon Germany. Two events now stand out in the historical perspective of today. Of course, one was the surging dominance of Hitler's might. The other was an experiment in the Kaiser-Wilhelm Institute in Berlin—the splitting of the uranium atom.

The world will not soon forget the madness of Hitler but it will never forget the cleavage of the atom. Wise Greeks had named it "atom," meaning "that which is indivisible," and this notion persisted even in the minds of the two German scientists who split the atom shortly before Christmas of that very year when the Third Reich absorbed Austria and Czechoslovakia. Both the latter events were to have their impact upon the atom.

Unfortunately, we cannot plunge into a description of the atom-splitting experiment, for it is understandable only if we relate it to events in England, France, Italy and other countries. The discovery of uranium fission turned out to be a rather hop-skip-and-jump affair. Much to my surprise I found that many facts in this dramatic sequence are unknown to scientists in this country. It was only after two trips to Europe that I managed to unravel part of the mystery surrounding the origin of the momentous discovery.

Most discoveries in science have their portents, and fission was to be no exception. Each scientist builds upon the foundation laid by his colleagues or their predecessors. I shall not go back to the days of the

Greeks or even before the turn of the century to identify these foundation stones. Rather I shall remark on Professor Einstein's most fundamental contribution to the substratum of modern physics and then dispense with the ancient history of atomic energy.

Even Albert Einstein had the way paved for his ecliptic theory of relativity, but to the public his now famous $E=mc^2$ relating mass and energy came out of the blue in 1905. At that time the famous man of our century was working as an obscure clerk in the Swiss patent office at Berne. His job was to examine patent papers and this he did, being careful to keep them in a large drawer in his desk. But the desk had another drawer which the budding scientist reserved for his calculations on his new theory. When his superior was not around, the young Einstein turned his attention to the papers in "his" drawer. He would then hurriedly shuffle them back and turn his attention to the contents of the other drawer when his boss appeared. This will probably rank as the greatest sleight-of-hand performance in history.

Einstein's fundamental contribution was, indeed, the theoretical basis for atomic energy. Much to his dismay it was to bear fruit forty years later in the perfection of an atomic bomb. But for many years Einstein's steppingstone remained unused, almost unnoticed. Man's knowledge of the composition of matter was too meager for him to dream of tapping the atom's energy.

A British discovery in 1932 triggered events which six years later led to the splitting of the uranium atom. Not directly, of course, but in a very zigzig fashion.

The man who gets the credit for this pivotal discovery of the "trigger" is Sir James Chadwick. Chadwick, a laconic, stiff-backed man, discovered a fundamental building block of matter called the neutron, which Lord Rutherford had predicted twelve years earlier.

An experimental physicist, Chadwick was on the trail of the neutron as early as 1924 but the scent grew cold. Six years later the search shifted to Germany where two researchers reported observing rays which were produced when beryllium, a light element used in copper alloys, was exposed to some radium material. The two Germans, Professors Bothe and Becker, were deeply puzzled by the X-ray-like quality of the new radiation but they did not link it to the neutron. Then the scene shifted to Paris, where Irene Curie and her husband Frederic Joliot-Curie (he annexed the famous name upon his marriage) were equally puzzled by the mysterious rays. The year was 1932.

Irene Curie was following in the footsteps of her famous mother, Madame Curie, the co-discoverer of radium. And like her mother, she was to die of cancer produced by the nature of her work with penetrating radiation. Her husband, the intense scientist, was to become fanatically devoted to the cause of Communism and to end a brilliant career as a disgruntled, broken man. But the days of the early thirties were sunny for them as they worked side by side in the laboratory. Something big was afoot and they were hot on the trail. There is no question but that the Joliot-Curies should have discovered the neutron. Certainly, they produced them in their experiments but they did not recognize them. In fact, Joliot-Curie later said that if he had known of Rutherford's work in England he would have discovered the new particle.

Chadwick, quite naturally, was thoroughly familiar with Rutherford's work and, as we have pointed out, he was hunting for the neutron as early as 1924. The hunt ended in 1932, as he explained the puzzling results of the German and French experimenters by proving that the mysterious radiation was the neutron, itself.

In 1934 the Joliot-Curies made a spectacular discovery which won them world fame and a Nobel prize. Working with a small source of a radium substance and a rather decrepit Geiger counter, they irradiated a thin aluminum foil. To their surprise the aluminum foil, itself, became radioactive and continued to give off rays even when removed to the next room. They repeated the experiment with other light elements such as magnesium and boron. Again the same results; the foils became active and emitted radioactive rays long after the original bombardment. Radioactivity had been produced artificially, and the pair of researchers proudly announced their discovery.

The irony of this discovery, made early in 1934, was that men like Professor E. O. Lawrence at the University of California had artificial radioactivity practically burning their fingers several years earlier. The dynamic Lawrence and a colleague, M. Stanley Livingston, had constructed an atom-smasher back in 1931, and subsequently other larger machines were built. They produced considerable artificial radioactivity but did not look for it. Had they done so, they could not have helped but discover what was right at hand. At the time the inventor of the atom-smashing cyclotron was busy raising funds and building up his staff for the now famous Radiation Laboratory which is perched high above the beautiful University of California campus, overlooking the San Francisco bay.

While cyclotrons were being developed and the exciting new discoveries were taking place, a young Italian physicist, Enrico Fermi, was rising to top rank among theoreticians in Europe. Stimulated by the events in France and England, thirty-three-year-old Fermi turned aside from his preoccupation with theory and began experimenting in the laboratory at Rome. Neutrons fascinated him, and soon he rounded up a crew of young colleagues eager to make a concerted attack upon the puzzling behavior of these newly discovered particles. Fermi was quick to sense that the tiny particles would be extremely powerful tools in the exploration of the interior of atoms. His ever alert brain had been occupied for some years exploring into the innermost crevices of the atomic core (technically, nucleus) and now Fermi turned to neutrons for bombardment of the nucleus and its mysteries.

Fermi's workday exhausted his companions. Appearing promptly in the laboratory at eight in the morning (a great shock to theoretical physicists who habitually sleep late!), he would work steadily until one. There followed lunch and siesta until 3 P.M. Then a five-hour stretch of intense research. Despite the fact that Fermi's workday began at 4 A.M. (he suffered from insomnia), he seemed tireless. Each day work began with a carefully thought-out analysis of previous work and a plan for new experiments.

Neutrons were used for bombardment of everything under the sun. Beginning with hydrogen, Fermi persisted until he found that neutrons would produce artificial activity in fluorine, the ninth element tried. Systematically, he continued bombarding all other elements until at last he came to element 92—uranium. In making these bombardments the Italian group had discovered that neutrons slowed down in water or paraffin became highly potent projectiles and were much more effective than fast neutrons. Upon subjecting uranium to a bath of slow neutrons, it was found that the irradiated uranium exhibited a number of different radioactivities. Fermi came up with this explanation: the uranium core or nucleus swallowed up the slow neutron and became a superheavy, unstable form of uranium not previously found in nature. This, in turn, would emit a charged particle and transform itself into element 93—a brand-new element never seen on earth before. Similarly, this newly created element would be unstable and decay to form different atoms (i.e., isotopes) of element 94 and so forth. A whole new series of transuranium isotopes was thus created!

The discovery of these new non-earthly elements was announced in 1934, and overnight scientists in many countries repeated the Italian experiments to examine the characteristics of transuranium atoms. This was certainly not a wild-goose chase, but certainly the weight of Fermi's authority in the field of nuclear science put other researchers off the track, as we shall see shortly.

One lone woman in Germany questioned what

Fermi had announced. Writing in *Allgemeine Zeitschrift für Chemie,* Ida Noddack criticized the great Fermi. "It is possible," wrote the German chemist, "that in the bombardment of heavy nuclei with neutrons, these nuclei disintegrate into several big fragments which are really isotopes of known elements. . . ." Frau Noddack shared credit with her husband for the discovery of rhenium, which is element number 75, so she could not be dismissed as a harmless kibitzer. No one seemed to pay any heed to her contention that Fermi may have erred, so she persuaded her husband to buttonhole his good friend, Professor Otto Hahn, at the Kaiser-Wilhelm Institute in Berlin.

Dr. Hahn, destined to play a leading role in the drama of the discovery of fission, listened to his good friend. Wearing the deceptive mask of a hard, almost militant, taskmaster, the former Chemical Corps officer puffed on a cigar and impatiently brushed aside the suggestion of the uranium atom being split, saying in effect, "It's impossible." An excellent teacher and also a student of Rutherford's, the German chemist rejected the idea, although his words to Noddack were soft and conciliatory. Better not mention this wild idea again, warned the clear-eyed Hahn, lest you never live it down. Had the chemistry teacher kept a completely open mind and subjected the revolutionary idea to laboratory test, how easy it would have been to discover fission. At that time the Kaiser-Wilhelm Institute boasted of a new science building complete with a high-energy atom-smasher. Its bulbous tower projected from the roof and gave the building a distinctive appearance in its setting in a quiet residential area of

Berlin. Today, neither the building nor Dr. Hahn remain in Berlin; the former having been demolished by bombing during the war, and the latter having left to become the distinguished director of the Max Planck Institute at Göttingen.

One wonders if the aging Professor Hahn really regrets his failure to act on Noddack's advice. He is a deeply moral man in addition to being a dedicated scientist. Supposing this man had discovered the secret of uranium energy in 1935; what course might history have taken then? With the rest of the world, particularly America, skeptical of Hitler's ambitions, Nazi Germany might have succeeded in being the first to command the power of the atom. One thing is clear— had the Nazis seized upon the promise of the split atom, then they would never have bent Dr. Hahn to their will for he would have taken his life first.

Hahn's two assistants at the Institute were Austrian-born Lise Meitner, a brilliant Jewess skilled in chemistry and physics, and Frederic Strassmann, a round, jolly chemist. A very hardheaded, difficult to convince woman, Frau Meitner guided both Hahn and Strassmann in theoretical aspects of nuclear physics. Strassmann, as junior partner in the firm, worked "downstairs" in the laboratory doing much of the dirty work. His gentle nature and fondness for telling stories belied his bitter opposition to the Nazis. Never once would he raise his arm in salute to der Fuehrer, even though this adamant refusal on his part did embarrass his colleagues.

Hahn, Meitner and Strassmann worked together as a team; this, despite the fact that persecution of the

Jews mounted in Germany. Frau Meitner stayed on in Berlin because of a technicality. She was an Austrian not a German Jew—a technicality which gave her temporary refuge in Berlin. The team became interested in Fermi's experiments as a natural outgrowth of the long experience which both Hahn and Meitner had in atomic research. Professor Hahn had begun his work in organic chemistry, but switched to research on radium and its compounds while in England and Canada. Lise Meitner had done some radioactivity work in Vienna before she joined up with Hahn in Berlin. This famous team was established in the fall of 1907 during a "short vacation" which Viennese Meitner planned. Discouraged, because women were not permitted to work in the Fischer institute in Berlin, Meitner appealed to Hahn and he arranged with the director to allow Frau Meitner to work in a woodworking shop in the basement—on one condition, however—that she stay "downstairs" and not invade the masculine sanctity "upstairs." The short vacation stretched out over a period of three decades, and the partnership is still held together by bonds of mutual respect and friendship.

We shall return to Berlin and to the anti-Nazi trio of scientists shortly. Let us look in on some fascinating and frustrating experiments conducted at Professor Lawrence's Radiation Laboratory in California, shortly after Fermi startled the scientific world with his announcement of transuranium elements.

Professor Lawrence's fame as inventor of the cyclotron was already serving as a magnet to draw brilliant embryonic scientists to the colorful campus of the University of California. A huge (by standards of the thirties) cyclotron had been built and Lawrence had succeeded in getting a powerful five-million-volt beam of nuclear particles. Such was the lowly beginning of the Radiation Laboratory, which today operates on a multimillion-dollar annual budget. In those days, as today, Lawrence had a dozen projects on the fire. He always had more projects than money, even though research budgets then were measured in hundreds of dollars.

A young chemist, who had just gotten his master's degree at Washington State College, was attracted to the Radiation Laboratory in 1935. Slow-speaking, gentle-natured Philip Abelson won a fellowship under Lawrence and started work on his Ph.D. degree. His work schedule was tough, for he spent fifty to sixty hours helping to run the cyclotron, while trying to cram in study time on his courses. The result was that he had practically no time to study.

In the spring of 1936 Lawrence was deeply puzzled by rereading the Fermi experiments in Rome, and expressed his concern that something seemed wrong. Approaching Abelson, he said, "You know chemistry, why not look into what Fermi has done?" Together they bombarded some uranium with slow neutrons produced with the aid of the cyclotron, but Lawrence did not find what he was looking for and left young Ableson to sweat it out for himself.

Ableson had married a medical student and was trying to exist on the princely stipend of sixty dollars a month. Trying to make ends meet was tough, but so was his nuclear research. Systematically, he repeated

Fermi's experiment irradiating uranium with neutrons. He had to fight to get "cyclotron time" because higher ranking scientists had "more important" work to do. Ableson was on the bottom of the seniority list and so he squeezed in his hours after dark when others were asleep. Just as the Italian experimenters had found certain radioactive substances and identified each as having its own nuclear personality, or rate of decay, the young Washingtonian also found the same substances in solutions he processed chemically from the irradiated uranium. Six or seven different substances showed up, and he attributed these to elements lying beyond uranium just as Fermi had done. But Abelson had his doubts.

In the fall of 1938, he talked his problem over with the adventurous, fast-talking Luis Alvarez, son of the famous physician. Alvarez was intrigued with the work and advised, "The most important thing you can do is to continue your work with neutrons and uranium." Ableson, encouraged by this advice, decided to shoot the works. He made one of his rare off-campus trips and visited San Fransisco. There he parted with twenty dollars of his own money, one-third of his monthly pay, and purchased ten pounds of crude uranium oxide—a yellowish impure compound which he proceeded to purify. Late that October, he started bombarding his big sample of uranium, running the cyclotron from 6 P.M. until 9 A.M.—hours which no one envied him. Sleepy-eyed, he would take the irradiated uranium and process it chemically—searching for products which he could identify. This time he had a new angle. He had a special type of instrument, called a crystal spectograph, which could analyze the X rays emitted from his irradiated uranium with such precision as to pin down precisely what element was producing the radiation. Fate was unkind to young Ableson, for about a week before he hit pay dirt in his research the news reached America that the uranium atom had been split.

To return to Europe where the atom was split late in 1938, we find an argument between the French and the Germans. Not unusual, of course, especially in the tense days when Hitler was appropriating real estate in Central Europe, but in this case the argument was over an interpretation of Fermi's experiment. Early that year the Austrian-German trio, Hahn, Meitner and Strassmann, repeated Fermi's experiments with uranium. They found the transuranium elements and in addition they obtained some puzzling new activities which they ascribed to elements 88 and 89, radium and actinium respectively. Note that they were reluctant to get very far off base from uranium, and they thought that "allowable" nuclear reactions might lead to the production of radium and also actinium.

In Paris, Irene Curie worked together with a Yugoslav chemist, Savitch, paralleling the experiments in Berlin. They focused attention upon a certain radioactivity which the German group attributed to actinium, and proved to their own satisfaction that it could not be actinium. What was it? They thought that the element behaved like lanthanum, an element lying next to barium in the periodic system of elements.

A report of the Curie-Savitch work reached Berlin in the early fall of 1938 and thoroughly upset Hahn and

Strassmann. Lise Meitner would, no doubt, have been upset, too, but with the annexation of Austria she became a German Jew and was forced to flee. Her colleagues conspired to sneak her out of the country into Holland where she fled to Stockholm. Professor Hahn was particularly shaken by the French challenge to his work and stubbornly refused to believe that *he* was wrong. *They* must be wrong, he reasoned, for it's impossible that they could be right. German and French chemists were quarreling over the identification of an element, spawned by irradiating uranium with neutrons, while Prime Minister Neville Chamberlin met with Adolf Hitler. No newspapers paid any attention to the elemental argument between the two pairs of scientists. Yet hidden in the argument was the spark that would someday set the world aflame.

The junior member of the team finally got Hahn, his senior partner, to repeat their chemical analysis. Perhaps, argued Strassmann, there might be something in what the French have found—or claim that they have found. With traditional Germanic thoroughness, the two went to work in the basement of the Institute. It was about a week before Christmas when they finally convinced themselves that their original conclusions were wrong. What they had thought was radium and actinium (elements 88 and 89) turned out to be barium and lanthanum (elements 56 and 57).

Here, indeed, was a puzzle. How in the world did element 56 get produced by bombarding element 92? What kind of weird alchemy accounted for the origin of barium? It was almost as though the atom had been cleaved in half. In fact, in the paper that Hahn and

Strassmann rushed to prepare, they actually had the right idea for they wrote: "The sum of the mass numbers for barium and manganese, for example, is 138+101, which adds up to 239. . . ." This equaled the mass of the original U^{238} atom plus a neutron. The two chemists were excited and hurriedly completed their Letter to the Editor of the *Naturwissenshaften*, a highly respected German scientific magazine. Communicating directly with the editor, they urged that space be held for their article and promptly dispatched it to his office. The only person to receive a copy of that famous letter was their old friend Lise Meitner.

Hahn and Strassmann had sent off their letter three days before Christmas in 1938. What they had found disturbed Hahn profoundly. Even though they had been very cautious in their conclusions, the great chemist worried. Their results proved that the uranium atom had split in two parts, but they had balked, stating: "We cannot yet bring ourselves to this step, which was in opposition to all previous experience in nuclear physics. It is yet possible that a series of strange and deceptive accidents could have produced the results we obtained." The article went to press but Hahn became more worried, exclaiming to Strassmann, "We are the biggest fools." He said that they had made a mistake and would gladly have recalled the article, but it was too late.

Lise Meitner, the lonely refugee, had decided to spend Christmas in Göteborg, a seaport in southwestern Sweden. Her nephew, Dr. Otto Frisch, on the staff at the Institute of Theoretical Physics at Copenhagen, journeyed two hundred miles to the north to be with her during the holidays. Neither of the two had any idea that Hahn and Strassmann were sending them a most unusual Christmas present—a copy of their letter.

Meitner and Frisch spent the holidays working furiously over the meaning of the Hahn-Strassmann letter. They developed a theory to fit the facts. It seemed hard to believe that the ramparts of the uranium atom had been breached, yet the chemical evidence from Berlin was indisputable. Physical theory had always rejected the concept of a massive disruption of the uranium nucleus; but perhaps there might be a new theory that would explain the unexpected experimental findings. Fortunately, Niels Bohr who headed up the Institute at Copenhagen, had just developed a model of the nucleus which treated it as though it were a drop of liquid. Putting their heads together, they dreamed up a new theory based upon this "liquid drop" model. It was clear to both of them that this new disruptive process in uranium should release a great deal of energy and so, when Otto Frisch went back to Copenhagen, he was primed to do some laboratory experiments to measure this energy release. In the meantime Lise Meitner would put the finishing touches on her theory. The two would keep in touch by telephone.

Frisch could hardly wait to tell Dr. Bohr the exciting news. When he did, the celebrated physicist clapped his hands to his head and in a high-pitched voice exclaimed, "Why did we not ever think of it?" Otto Frisch, who sometimes was more attracted to music than to physics, propelled himself into uranium research. He kept in touch with Frau Meitner in Stockholm by long-distance phone; she was difficult to convince and he spent a small fortune in phone bills before they agreed upon their scientific paper. Niels Bohr, their guiding light, left for America to visit his friend Einstein at Princeton before their paper was finished, but he took with him the essential facts about the new phenomenon. It was partly due to Bohr that the splitting of the atom was named "fission," for he had a long-abiding interest in biological science and the name, a biological term for the process of cell division, originated from conversation between a mutual friend and piano-playing Otto Frisch.

The Meitner-Frisch scientific paper took the form of a Letter to the Editor of *Nature,* a British scientific magazine. The letter, dated January 16, 1939, appeared in the February 11 issue of *Nature* under the title "Disintegration of Uranium by Neutrons: A New Type of Nuclear Reaction."

Nuclear fission finally saw the light of day! For four years everyone, including Fermi and scientists in half a dozen countries, had missed the boat. Even when Hahn and Strassmann were on the right boat they were almost shanghaied aboard, and it took Meitner and Frisch to see clearly the name of the boat.

chapter 2

TAMING THE CHAIN REACTION

One might think that the splitting of the atom was the open-sesame to atomic energy. This is not quite true.

Splitting a single atom like uranium does release a large amount of energy although we must put this on a relative scale. Even a billion uranium atoms exploding at the same time produce less bang than a tiny ladyfinger firecracker. To make a real dent upon the world an astronomic number of atoms must be fissioned.

The gifted pianist-physicist Otto Frisch was the first to measure the energy released by the disintegration of a uranium atom. He used electronic devices to record the violent outward thrust of the two split halves of the atom as they hurtled apart. His apparatus timed the speed of these projectiles at roughly ten thousand miles per second. However, his equipment was a laboratory curiosity so far as the practical release of atom energy was concerned, for he put in more power than he got out and he had no way to use the output power.

Neither Hahn nor Strassmann had any notion that their atom-splitting experiment was of great importance. Interesting, yes, most intriguing; but important? —no.

There had to be some connecting link—some means by which a large number of atoms could be split in succession. A few scientists, such as Austrian-born

Frederic Houtermans, had speculated about such things shortly after the neutron was discovered in 1932. But it was casual shop talk which was never dignified in print or in experiment.

The real open-sesame to atomic energy *is* the neutron. To make this clear we go back to the first thoughts which Enrico Fermi had on hearing that the uranium atom had been split. The swarthy Italian physicist, who had experimented so ingeniously with neutrons back in Rome during the year 1934, had hardly settled his family in New York City when he received the all-important news in January, 1939. A friend, returning from a lecture at Princeton, rushed into the Pupin Physics Laboratory on the campus of Columbia University and blurted out that the atom had been split. He said that Dr. Niels Bohr, who arrived on January 16 from Denmark, had revealed the news of the Hahn-Strassmann experiments together with the Meitner-Frisch interpretation of them.

Fermi bubbled with ideas and explained them to his young associate Herbert Anderson. Dr. Anderson had just made a deal with Fermi; he would teach Fermi English and in return Fermi would teach him physics. Fermi proceeded to teach: "Let me explain this business of the fission of uranium," he started out, his rollicking Italian dialect all too much in evidence. Then he continued with that eagerness which always infected his listeners:

The neutron enters and causes an instability in the uranium nucleus and it's split apart. A great deal of energy is released, as Otto Frisch has shown. But the circumstances are those in which, in all probability, neutrons will be emitted as well and this is at the root of the matter. For if the neutrons are emitted in greater number than they are absorbed, a chain reaction will be possible and the way to a new source of energy will have been found.

It was characteristic of Fermi to plunge directly to the core of the problem as so strikingly demonstrated in this instance. True to form, he wasted little time wondering about the neutrons. He urged his youthful English teacher, "Come and help me find these neutrons. Let us measure their absorption and their emission with some care so that we can understand these processes in detail and know how to proceed."

Fermi and Anderson formed a team until Fermi's untimely death late in 1954. At the time the partnership began there were two other great scientists at Columbia. One was Dr. Walter Zinn, Canadian-born schoolteacher who was attracted to nuclear research. The other was a most unusual scholar from Hungary —one of a quartet of stellar physicists originating there. His name is Leo Szilard. Fermi once described him most aptly: "He is certainly a very peculiar man, extremely intelligent. He is extremely brilliant and he seems somewhat to enjoy, at least that is the impression that he gives to me, he seems to enjoy startling people."

Szilard certainly startled Fermi early that winter of 1939. Convinced that what Fermi, Zinn, Anderson and he were doing was destined to be of world-shaking significance, Szilard approached Fermi with a proposition. He urged him and his colleagues to publish their work privately—to keep it out of print where it might be helpful to the Germans. Szilard told me that Fermi was shocked by this proposal and at first did not like the idea since it was so utterly foreign to the tradition of free and open publication. This initial rebuff did not stop Szilard for he sent letters and telegrams to many researchers pleading with them to keep their results secret. Thus, in a very real sense it was Szilard who was the inventor of atomic secrecy. Szilard showed me a letter, dated February 2, 1939, addressed to Professor M. Joliot in Paris, in which he described the chain reaction and warned: "In certain circumstances this might lead to the construction of bombs which would be extremely dangerous in general and particularly in the hands of certain governments." Note how quickly scientists had looked beyond the discovery of fission to the release of atomic energy. It took Szilard only two weeks to put his thoughts on paper although I know he had the idea earlier.

We must now make a slight excursion into the past, going back to 1935 for some most pertinent information about uranium. We have been talking about uranium as if it were composed of only one kind of atom. We are now backtracking to 1935 to describe a critical experiment performed by Arthur J. Dempster. It was my good fortune to work with Dr. Dempster for several years, and thus I can relate from my own experience the nature of his work on uranium atoms.

Dr. Dempster was a shy, small-statured man who spent his whole life weighing atoms. At the end of World War I, he designed an instrument called a mass spectograph which sorts out atoms of various weight and allows them to be registered on a piece of photographic plate inserted into the machine. If you take a small sample of an element like tin and analyze it with this atom-weighing device, you will discover there are ten different kinds of tin atoms. That is to say, ten atoms of the same element which are the same chemically but which differ in weight. We call such atoms isotopes. Some elements like gold have only one isotope. We symbolize this isotope by a kind of shorthand—Au^{197}—the chemical symbol being Au and the superscript being the weight of the atom.

Early in the summer of 1935, Dr. Dempster focused his attention upon uranium. Working in a darkened room on the University of Chicago campus, directly opposite the tennis courts, the Canadian-born physicist took a piece of brown-black uranium no larger than the end of a lead pencil and carefully mounted it in a metallic holder. Then he sealed the assembly into his machine with only the glow of a small gas flame illuminating the room; the flame being used to melt sealing wax and make his instrument vacuum-tight. He turned on a powerful electrical discharge and the tiny rod of uranium metal spluttered into an incandescent arc, lighting up the room with an unreal flickering light. I shall always remember Dr. Dempster in this role, absorbed and delighted in his work, hovering solicitously over his machine. It was during hours like these, which I shared with him in the solitude of his laboratory, that his shyness disappeared and he talked freely. Thus, I know that on the day he sparked his bit of uranium and fed its atoms into his instrument, he had no notion that anything momentous was in the offing.

Quietly Dempster ended the experiment, flipped the

high-voltage switch, cut off the intense magnetic field and groped inside the gadget for the photographic plate which he hoped would show up the atoms of uranium. Slipping it into a wooden box and hastily wrapping it in black cloth, he walked through his tiny adjoining office into what was later my office and ducked into the photographic darkroom. Into the developer went the 1-by-4-inch glass plate which was jagged on one corner where Dempster had broken it. Then a quick immersion in the hypo solution and he impatiently snapped on the lights, not caring to wait for the fog to clear from the emulsion.

A heavy black line stood out against the milky whiteness of the plate. Dempster held the plate up to the light and looked closer. There next to the dense line was another fainter one. He dunked it back in the hypo to clear and walked back to his office. It may not belong to uranium, he mused, knowing out of long experience the peculiarities of his gadget. It might be some impurity which got mixed up with uranium in spite of his precautions. The proof of the pudding would come from careful measurement of the plate with a microscope. Later when he measured the plate he discovered that the faint line corresponded to a scarce variant of uranium. There were actually two kinds. Just as tin had ten and gold had one, uranium had two isotopes. The most abundant one he measured as 238 times heavier than hydrogen and the scarce isotope was lighter; it was U^{235}. It turned out that ordinary uranium contained only 1 part of the scarce variety to 139 parts of the heavy form. Put another way, uranium was 99.3 per cent U^{238} and 0.7 per cent U^{235}.

Dempster had discovered another isotope, but this was not startling, for he had many such discoveries to his credit. Uranium was not of any particular importance in the world, and the physics professor had no prescience that it would be an earth-shaker. As a scientist, Dempster had filled in another missing page in the bulging tome of science. Sometime in the future this contribution to pure science might be useful. As we already know the future turned out to be the year 1939.

Returning now to Fermi and his colleagues at Columbia, it should be almost obvious that these scientists needed some more pages from the book of pure science. Specifically, they had to know which form of uranium was responsible for fission. The abundant U^{238} or the rare U^{235}?

Two men teamed up to give the preliminary answer to this question. The famous Dr. Bohr from Copenhagen joined up with his American friend, the remarkable John A. Wheeler. Only twenty-eight years old at the time, Wheeler was happy to see his Danish teacher with whom he had worked in Copenhagen a few years before. For his part, the shrill-voiced genius, Dr. Bohr, could not have chosen a better collaborator. Both theoretical physicists, they pooled their brain power and soon came up with their answer. They were sure that U^{235} was the culprit.

Physicists respected the theoretical answer but they had to have experimental proof. Another team of scientists went to work. This was an all-American team composed of Alfred Nier from the University of Minnesota and two Columbia physicists, John Dunning and

Eugene Booth, Jr., a Rhodes scholar. Dr. Dunning was later to become dean of engineering at Columbia. Dr. Nier used a mass spectrograph of somewhat different design from Dempster's to separate a tiny quantity of U^{235}. More, much more, was needed that the insignificant amount which had blackened Dempster's photographic plate. Nier succeeded in catching the all-important U^{235} on a tiny flat needle. He handed this over to his teammates and they proceeded to bombard it with neutrons just as Hahn and Strassman had done the year before. Comparing the results of bombarding the separated U^{235} with those for ordinary uranium, they proved that Bohr and Wheeler were correct. U^{235} was responsible for fission.

This fact made the achievement of a chain reaction more difficult, and there is no better way to express the difficulty than to revert to Fermi's statement of it:

The fundamental point in fabricating a chain reacting machine is of course to see to it that each fission produces a certain number of neutrons and some of these neutrons will again produce fission. If an original fission causes more than one subsequent fission then of course the reaction goes. If an original fission causes less than one subsequent fission then the reaction does not go.

Fermi then spelled out the problem in more detail, grinning as he talked, completely relaxed, happy in the dual role of teacher-researcher.

Now, if you take the isolated pure isotope U^{235}, you may expect that the unavoidable losses of neutrons will be minor, and therefore if in the fission somewhat more than one neutron is emitted then it will be merely a matter of piling up enough uranium–235 to obtain a chain reacting structure. But if to each gram of uranium–235 you add some 140 grams of uranium–238 that come naturally with it, then the competition will be greater, because there will be all this ballast ready to snatch away the not too abundant neutrons that come out in the fission and therefore it was clear that one of the ways to make possible the production of a chain reaction was to isolate the isotope U^{235} from the much more abundant isotope U^{238}.

Judging from this analysis by Fermi, the road ahead looked straightforward, even though long and uphill all the way. The direct route seemed to be separation of the valuable U^{235} from natural uranium. Professor Harold Urey, Nobel prizeman of heavy hydrogen fame, spearheaded this separation project at Columbia.

But, perhaps there was another road to take, Fermi reasoned. Perhaps, as he put it, ". . . one might be able to achieve a chain reaction without having to separate the isotopes." The thirty-eight-year-old physicist had in mind a machine made of ordinary uranium—a chain reacting machine. The task Fermi later described as "almost beyond human possibilities." He relished the challenge and plunged into experimental work with Szilard, Zinn and Anderson. They worked together on the seventh floor of the Pupin Physics Laboratory which overlooks Broadway and 118th Street in New York City.

The Italian-American-Hungarian-Canadian foursome was a varied composite of personalities. Fermi, the unquestioned leader, always pushing ahead, discarding idea after idea, restlessly searching for bits of data about neutrons. Zinn, tall, sandy-haired, a down-to-earth type with practical knowledge of the world. Anderson, typically American, with close-cropped dark hair, taciturn, always ready to listen to Fermi and to work any hour of the day. And, of course, Szilard—the unpredictable. Rotund, short in stature, pink in complexion, Szilard had his finger in many pies.

They needed neutrons. Szilard promoted this as he did so many other things by borrowing two thousand dollars to rent a radium source. It never occurred to him to ask the U.S. government for funds. Today we take a two-billion-dollar AEC budget in our stride, but back in 1939 Szilard had to go out and borrow the money for some radium. He got it and the group was in business—they had neutrons. These slippery nuclear particles are produced when the rays from radium strike the light element, beryllium. It was a feeble source of neutrons—an aspirin-sized piece of radium and a half pound of beryllium. Their uranium, five hundred pounds of it, came from the Eldorado Radium Corporation.

Here was the problem they sought to solve. They had to find some way to keep the neutrons from being swallowed up by the abundant U^{238} and yet get them to fission U^{235}. Neutrons produced by the fissioning uranium are very fast initially. If one stacks up solid uranium in a great pile these neutrons would be captured in the U^{238} and thus robbed from splitting U^{235}. The task was to find some substance to mix with uranium so that the neutrons would miss U^{238} and hit U^{235}. This could best be accomplished, according to calculations, if the neutrons bounced around for a while and spent their energy. When they were much slower they could still split U^{235} yet they would not be so susceptible to capture in U^{238}. This was really much trickier than it sounds, especially since the Columbia physicists had lots to learn about the peculiar behavior of bouncing neutrons.

Water looked good but measurements discouraged the group and they turned to graphite as the best bet for slowing down or moderating the neutrons. There was, however, a real difficulty. Water was cheap and the experiments were quickly done. Graphite was another matter; it had to be pure and lots of it would be needed. Money would be required for this research, so Szilard again turned entrepreneur.

Initial efforts to interest the government in the nuclear work were not encouraging so Szilard took a high-level approach. It was Szilard who moved behind the scenes, persuading his friend Albert Einstein to sign his now-famous letter to President Roosevelt. Both were intensely worried about the possibility that Germany might be forging ahead in the race for atomic energy. After all, the initial experiments had taken place in Berlin. Moreover, a very ominous new note was struck—Hitler slapped an embargo on all Czechoslovakian uranium. Szilard was filled with an overwhelming sense of doom that summer of 1939—and Einstein was quick to share his anxiety. For the sake of the record it is well to add that three other European scientists were equally concerned and influenced Einstein at this time. The trio included Eugene P. Wigner, slightly built, soft-voiced Hungarian engineer turned physicist; Edward Teller, later renowned for his H-bomb activity; and the brilliant Victor Weisskopf, now at M.I.T. and probably the most globe-circling physicist in this country.

The letter Einstein signed was addressed to "F.D. Roosevelt" and began: "Sir: Some recent work by E. Fermi and L. Szilard . . . leads me to expect that the element of uranium may be turned into a new and important source of energy in the immediate future . . . it may become possible to set up a nuclear chain reaction in a large mass of uranium, by which vast amounts of power and large quantities of new radium-like elements would be generated. Now it appears almost certain that this could be achieved in the immediate future." The letter went on: "This new phenomenon would also lead to construction of bombs, and it is conceivable—though much less certain—that extremely powerful bombs of a new type may thus be constructed." This historic document, dated August 2, 1939, was signed "A. Einstein."

A memorandum signed by Szilard (August 15, 1939) was prepared to accompany Einstein's letter. Both were entrusted to Szilard's contact on Wall Street—Dr. Alexander Sachs. The latter was a confidant of Roosevelt's and, in addition, was an avid student of international affairs. Dr. Sachs was at the time with the Lehman Investment Corporation. He visited the President the next month to persuade him of the urgency for pushing the atomic project. If there were any doubts in the President's mind they were resolved by the turn of world events; Hitler had lashed out at Poland and the world was at war. He acted to set up a special Uranium Committee, consisting of Dr. Lyman Briggs, the director of the Bureau of Standards, Colonel

K. F. Adamson of the Army Ordnance and Commander G. C. Hoover of the Navy's Ordnance. This committee met on October 21, 1939, and recommended among other things that Fermi be given four tons of graphite and fifty tons of uranium. The War Department, which six months earlier had evidenced little sympathy for an atomic bomb, made six thousand dollars available for the research.

Precious time had been wasted while scientists left their laboratories and spent their time in committee rooms. And more time would be wasted the next year. More committee meetings took place and cautious recommendations were forthcoming. The foreign-born scientists, driven by a sense of urgency, failed to communicate to American officials the need for speed. Szilard later told me, "Not a single experiment in the development of a chain reaction was performed from July 1, 1939, until the middle of March, 1940. I got fed up with the inaction." Thereupon he wrote a paper asserting that the chain reaction was possible and urged immediate action.

Meanwhile Fermi had gotten his uranium and graphite bricks to build an experimental "pile." This was merely to gain some knowledge to see if a chain reaction could be produced; they had no thought that these primitive experiments would actually produce a chain reaction. Small-scale experiments gave way to more impressive ones and the group had to look around for space. Dean Pegram at Columbia found it for them in Schermerhorn Hall on the campus. Then physicists, including the stocky Fermi, turned weight-lifters, hoisting up bricks of graphite to make a pile. The pile was a structure of graphite bricks interspersed with big cubical cans of uranium oxide. It was tough, dirty work and the scientists came home at night looking like coal miners. Dean Pegram again came to the rescue with the suggestion that they hire a dozen or so husky boys from the football squad. Fermi commented, "Well, we were reasonably strong, but I mean we were, after all, thinkers." Humor was always close to the surface in the neutron expert and he was quick to hire the football players and delighted in watching them pack the uranium in fifty- and hundred-pound cans.

These early experiments at Columbia helped to fill in the gaps in the brand-new science of neutron physics. Our focus upon Columbia should not be interpreted as meaning that no work went on elsewhere. Other laboratories in U.S.A. were showing interest in uranium research, but it was clear that the greatest progress was being achieved under Fermi's tutelage.

Across the Atlantic work went on in France and England. When France fell, some of the leading nuclear scientists fled to England where they continued their work. Communication between the British and Americans was very imperfect. Had there been closer liaison at this time, undoubtedly precious months could have been saved in the atomic development.

Fermi's intense concentration on achieving the chain reaction stemmed partly from his feeling that it would take a very long time to separate the valuable U^{235} from the worthless U^{238}. This being the case, we may ask what did Fermi see in the chain reaction? Undoubtedly, he saw in it a source of power, for this was mentioned by both Szilard and Einstein as being useful to the Navy, particularly for submarines. Fermi also knew that if a bomb were to be achieved, scientists would have to learn much more about the behavior of neutrons and the controlled pile would be a valuable proving ground for future bomb experts. But one wonders if Fermi did not have something else in mind— i.e., the original idea which he had back in 1935. Namely, the production of elements 93 and 94.

These transuranium elements, prematurely birthed in 1935, had still not been identified in 1939. In the spring of 1940 a discovery was made which gave new meaning and urgency to Fermi's preoccupation with the chain reaction. The discovery was made at the Radiation Laboratory in Berkeley where Philip Abelson, had missed the boat on nuclear fission. He had, however, completed his Ph.D. thesis on "The Products of Uranium Cleavage" and had gone off to Washington, D.C., in the summer of 1939 to help build a cyclotron at the Carnegie Institution's laboratory in the swank residential district off Connecticut Avenue. He left his wife in California to work on her medical training, and after a long winter in Washington, D.C., young Abelson decided to return to Berkeley for a week's vacation.

Upon his arrival in Berkeley, Abelson found that his friend, Edwin McMillan, a native Californian, had been bombarding uranium in a most ingenious manner. He arranged thin films of uranium so that when they were bombarded and fissioned, the split atoms would be knocked out of the foil. Thus, any uranium atoms which were not fissioned but which did succeed in capturing a neutron would be left behind in the film.

Chemical analysis of the irradiated uranium foil might therefore show up the presence of Fermi's long-sought-for transuranium elements. McMillan's stunt largely eliminated the confusion caused by the presence of all the split uranium atoms.

Abelson's long experience with the chemistry of uranium and its products plus McMillan's trick allowed the pair of them to do a whirlwind series of experiments. In three days they had identified element 93—later named neptunium. At long last Fermi's ideas had been vindicated. Man had finally succeeded in manufacturing a new element. But it did not stay around very long. Being very unstable, half of it disintegrates every 2¼ days, half of that disappears in another 2¼ days and so on until in two weeks there is not much left. Just as uranium is transformed to neptunium, the latter becomes element 94 which is plutonium. Lanky McMillan, as the physicist of the research twosome, searched for evidence of plutonium, but for some reason or other missed it, although he was on the right track.

Even before plutonium had been isolated scientists, like Dr. Louis Turner of Princeton, had pointed to it as being a potential competitor to U^{235}; in other words, a bomb material. Theoretical considerations showed that plutonium would be long-lived and similar to U^{235} in its nuclear personality, i.e., explosive.

Fermi's work with dullish brown uranium and greasy graphite now seemed much more important. A chain reacting machine (reactor) would be a fabulous source of neutrons. These might be used to bombard the worthless U^{238} and convert it into plutonium—a daring idea but one worth looking into since U^{235} separation seemed so dismally difficult.

Success in achieving the chain reaction hung upon a single figure, specifically, the number of neutrons evaporated from the splitting of a single uranium atom. This was an exceedingly elusive statistic to run down, and the prewar values were quoted as somewhere between 1 and 3.5. If only one neutron came off from a splitting atom, then the chain reaction was a futile dream for man could not perfect a machine capable of capturing every single neutron. Impurities in uranium, in graphite and in structural material as well as leakage from the reactor would rob neutrons from the chain reaction. Moreover, capture of neutrons in U^{238} would depress the reaction. If as many as three neutrons were emitted in fission, then things would be quite rosy although by no means a sure thing. This would give the scientists much more room for losing the neutrons and still have enough left to perpetuate the chain reaction.

The hard-working group of physicists at Columbia University now became very ambitious and boldly asked for more funds to buy graphite and uranium. In the summer of 1940 they asked for $140,000—a staggering sum but the project by then had the President's blessing and the money was made available. Money did not solve the problems, however, for the state of the art in 1940 was such that no pure uranium or graphite existed. And the purity specifications of the physicists astonished industrialists who were unaccustomed to orders which stipulated only microscopic traces of elements like boron. A year vanished as scientists and industrialists struggled with making really pure materials. Gradually the project was emerging from the idea stage and entering the hardware phase. Scientists like Szilard, Wigner and Fermi pressed for action.

Dr. James B. Conant, president of Harvard and Vannevar Bush's right-hand man on the atomic project, announced an "all-out" research effort on December 6, 1941. By a curious coincidence Dr. Conant revealed this momentous decision to a roomful of top scientists the day before Pearl Harbor. Two Columbia scientists, Urey and Pegram, had completed a visit to Britain. They learned that the British were optimistic about the bomb and at the same time they picked up the ominous news that the Nazis had placed large orders with Norway for the production of heavy water. This substance was known to be superior to graphite in its ability to conserve neutrons in a chain reaction. We concluded that we were in a race with the Germans for the bomb. The sense of urgency was underlined by the actual outbreak of war.

Nobel prizeman Arthur H. Compton of Chicago was chosen to head up work on the chain reaction. This was a most fortunate choice since he was respected by the scientific community and would attract new high-caliber recruits to the Plutonium Project. The latter was the name given to the work although it was hardly ever used even in secret meetings. Plutonium was usually referred to as "product." A decision was made to concentrate work at Chicago, and shortly afterward Fermi and his colleagues moved to the campus of the University. Their new laboratory was a network of buildings, parts of buildings and single rooms scattered throughout the campus. This was the Metallurgical Laboratory with headquarters in Eckart Hall—the very building where Arthur Dempster had discovered the all-important U^{235}.

I had been attracted to the University of Chicago because of A. H. Compton's fame in cosmic ray studies, so I was on campus when Fermi and company moved in. At the time I was completing my research for my doctor's degree and volunteered to join the project, but my boss, Compton, advised me to finish my work. The purpose of the secret project wasn't much of a secret to physicists. All you had to do was to look in the scientific literature to see a complete absence of papers on uranium fission and to look at the concentration of Nobel prize-winners on campus.

Space was hard to find on campus (I was doing my research in the wooden press box atop Stagg Field), and it was only natural for Fermi and his crew to end up in the abandoned squash courts under the West Stands of the football field. There, close to the corner of 57th and Ellis Avenue, the first large-scale graphite-uranium pile was assembled. "Pile" may not sound like a very dignified title for this chain reacting machine but it was descriptive. The original cubical array of graphite blocks interspersed with tons of uranium was not a very impressive sight—just a pile of ultra-refined coal.

Theoretical experts like Fermi, Wigner, Szilard and Wheeler had worked long and hard to provide a mathematical foundation for the chain reaction. The acrobatics of a neutron as it emerges fresh from fission and knocks around inside the pile required careful analysis.

The basic problem was to calculate how to place the uranium inside the graphite so that a chain reaction would take place. A group of about twenty physicists put their heads together in offices on the fourth floor of Eckart Hall to solve the problem. Later, Eugene P. Wigner, who has a peculiar habit of constantly bowing as he talks, remarked that the solution was "straightforward" and "one of the great surprises of the Plutonium Project was how easy it was." Laymen will be forgiven if they credit the scientist with excessive modesty for the problem which was juggled was not simple.

The first day in December, 1942, the pile was finally loaded but it remained quiescent for its throbbing pulse was inhibited by long "control rods" which were inserted into the graphite assembly. These rods were coated with material to absorb neutrons, i.e., as deliberate impurities placed in the machine. Laboratory tests indicated that the materials were pure enough, theory showed that the machine design should work and all was in readiness for the actual test. We shall let Fermi's closest friend, Herbert Anderson tell what happened:

When, on December 2, 1942, Enrico Fermi stood before that silent monster he was its acknowledged master. Whatever he commanded it obeyed. When he called for it to come alive and pour forth its neutrons, it responded with remarkable alacrity; and when at his command it quieted down again, it had become clear to all who watched that Fermi had indeed unlocked the door to the Atomic Age.

chapter 3

MAKING THE BOMB STUFF

Success at Chicago sent a surge of confidence throughout the atomic project. Few other such dramatic
climaxes were to occur in the history of the scientist's
work. This did not mean that ultimate success with the
bomb was now assured, but it did signal that the first
real milestone had been passed.

Word of the important news was telephoned to Dr.
James Conant on the East Coast. At the other end of
the line was Conant's good friend Arthur Compton,
project leader at Chicago.

Carefully avoiding any reference to secret data,
Compton said, "The Italian navigator has landed in
the New World."

Conant's reply was equally allegorical: "How were
the natives?" to which the Chicago physicist replied,
"Very friendly."

This brief exchange, incomprehensible to any wire-
tapper, told Conant what he needed to know. The
Plutonian Project could now be given high priority and
full speed ahead. Dr. Compton later told me that
Fermi's triumph came just in time to get the Plutonium
Project "under the wire." Had the December second
success been long postponed, top-level decisions might
have bypassed the chain reactor work in favor of the
Oak Ridge processes. Even a week's delay at this
critical time might have made a drastic difference.

Thus, it is that a single man like Fermi emerges

in history as critical to our society. There is no substitute for the spark of genius—especially in science.

President Roosevelt decided that the moment had arrived for an all-out production effort and he called together a few key members of Congress selected from the Appropriations Committees. They listened in awe as scientists intoned the foreign words of fission, chain reaction and atomic bomb. Their concern deepened as they were briefed upon the German counterpart of our Manhattan Project. They were told that the project had to be ultrasecret but that money was needed at once—at least a billion dollars. The eight members of Congress agreed to approve the funds, even though some of them must have questioned the constitutionality of the process.

Almost four years had passed since Fermi's personal "go-ahead" and that of Roosevelt. Sir James Chadwick summed it up: "It always takes time to grasp a new idea, to accept it, and to see its consequences, even an idea of one's own. It takes longer to convince other people, especially when the idea involves action on a big scale." The discoverer of the neutron went on to say that, in the summer of 1941: "We were satisfied that the project of making an atomic bomb was practicable and likely to lead to decisive results in the war." The British scientist estimated that about one whole year was lost in the early stages of decision-making.

General Leslie R. Groves had arrived on the scene as the War Department's Corps of Engineers took over the production phases of the atomic project under the coded heading "Manhattan Engineer District." High priority was assigned immediately to the Plutonium Project, and scientists intensified their work on designing higher power piles, or reactors as they later became known. The original West Stands pile was disassembled and shipped out to a new site on the outskirts of Chicago. The site was known as Argonne and was close to the present location of the Argonne National Laboratory. There the reactor was rebuilt and carefully shielded with a concrete wall to protect against the penetrating radiation emitted by the split atoms. The power of the rebuilt machine was boosted to a kilowatt or the equivalent of what an ordinary household demands in electrical power.

The tempo of the work schedule is indicated by the fact that new reactors were in design before others had been tested. It was decided in the interest of security to build the first cooled reactor at Oak Ridge, Tennessee, more popularly known as the dog patch. This thousand-kilowatt pile was built in record time, but even before it was finished the huge production piles were under design. In a sense there were no prototypes for the massive plutonium producers, since the Oak Ridge model was a hundred times less in power and, moreover, was cooled by pumping air through aluminum channels which contained uranium rods or "slugs." Like the Fermi pile at the West Stands, the Oak Ridge model was composed of graphite. But for the first time the engineers had a chance to try out the scheme of arranging the uranium in long cylinders throughout the graphite. This facilitated charging the structure with uranium slugs and simplified removal of the "hot" slugs—they were simply poked out the other end of the aluminum channel and allowed to fall into a hopper. This new type of geometry presented men like Wigner and Fermi with an entirely new set of problems which were much more difficult to solve than the original Chicago design.

When the critical experiment was being performed in the squash courts at Chicago at the end of 1942, engineers and du Pont officials were scouting the banks of the Columbia River in the state of Washington seeking out a likely place to locate the huge plutonium plants. Looking back on this telescoping of time, one wonders if the government or the du Pont company would have pushed ahead with plans for mammoth plants had they fully appreciated the nature of the unknown territory which the scientists were then exploring. Perhaps this was a good illustration of the saying: "Where ignorance is bliss, 'tis folly to be wise."

I hasten to add that this is not to accuse General Groves of ignorance. But he had assumed his duties on September 17, 1942, as head of the atomic project and he could scarcely have been fully indoctrinated into the mysteries of atomic energy by the end of that year. Yet early in 1943 some two hundred square miles of land was acquired adjoining the Columbia River, and on April 6 swarms of construction men invaded the sagebrush-studded, rolling country. A year later this raw camp had swollen to become the fourth largest city in the state of Washington. Before summer brought its scorching heat to the region near Hanford, Washington, men were at work setting the forms for the first of the three huge piles. This plant was successfully operated in the fall of the next year—a truly incredible feat of engineering when one considers many of the unknown or poorly known quantities involved in plant design.

Some of these unknown quantities are still not fully illuminated and form barriers to reactor engineering in the design of modern nuclear power plants even today. In the wartime years one of the sorest problems was that of "canning" the uranium slugs in aluminum jackets so that there would be a good thermal bond between the two metals and so that there would be no leaks in the jacket. One might not think offhand that cladding a piece of uranium in aluminum would be too much of a job, but as things turned out it was an exceedingly arduous task. Elaborate experiments were devised to check upon the tightness of the aluminum seal, and after much trial and error, a method was worked out that proved satisfactory.

No one knew, and theoreticians were at a loss to predict, how uranium and graphite would behave after being "cooked" in the pile for months. Splitting uranium atoms might disrupt the orderly arrangement of other atoms in the precious metal. Similarly, the fast-flying neutrons, flitting about in the graphite, might displace carbon atoms from their accustomed locations, causing unknown changes in the structure of the greasy black blocks. So great was the ignorance about this effect in graphite that anxiety grew and grew after the plants started to operate. Great scientists, like the kindly Dr. James Franck, worried constantly about what would happen to the graphite inside the huge piles. I recall that he calculated how energy was being stored up in the "graphite lattice" with each day's operation. "This energy," he said morosely, "must come out sometime. If it goes out too quickly . . ." He threw up his hands in a manner which required no further words. Actually, the greasy graphite did store up energy and ultimately swelled in size until the top of the huge structure was bowed out. Fortunately, however, the scientist-engineers found a way out by proper treatment of the graphite and by design of the structure.

Another severe worry was that of corrosion inside the pile. This was judged to be such a serious problem that all water pumped through the aluminum channels in the graphite structure was chemically purified before use. After the war we learned that the Soviets who designed similar plants did not resort to this refinement and apparently did not encounter serious trouble.

Not all of these technical difficulties have been licked even today, but we shall defer discussion of them to a later chapter when we resume our treatment of nuclear power.

Finally in the fall of 1944 the first Hanford plant was ready to swing into operation. The huge cubical array of graphite, all encased in its thick shield of concrete to protect personnel against the intense radiation, was loaded with many tons of uranium slugs. Cautiously, the cadmium-plated, neutron-absorbing control rods were withdrawn from the machine, and the designers were elated to see the machine "go critical." All went well as the reactor was slowly brought up to power. Then something queer and quite unexpected happened. The pile had been behav-

ing rather oddly for several days, and operators at
the control desk had had continually to readjust the
control rod settings, moving them farther and farther
out from the pile. It was thought at first that "mud"
from the water might be accumulating in the cooling
tubes or that some of the tubes were leaking water into
the graphite. To the consternation of the operators,
the pile stopped completely even though the control
rods were all the way out! One could not have imagined a more frightening situation. Then after the
pile was allowed to rest awhile, it would start up again
only to repeat its erratic performance as before. There
were gremlins in the chain reaction.

Fermi, slide rule in hand, walked into John Wheeler's
office and showed him a record of the peculiar cyclic
behavior of the machine. The young Princeton physicist, who had worked with the great Niels Bohr, had
been doing theoretical work on the fission products—
the two halves into which the uranium atom split. A
single uranium atom splits into a single pair—like the
barium and krypton pair we discussed earlier. But
each uranium fission produces its own partner atoms.
They may range over various combinations of thirty
different elements. Wheeler at once suspected that the
reason for the slowing up and stopping of the pile was
to be found in a poisoning effect due to the buildup
of fission products inside the pile.

Wheeler told Fermi that he thought the culprits
were krypton and xenon. Whereupon Fermi calculated
the effect and deduced that an isotope of xenon
(Xe^{135}) was guilty. A quick-decaying fission product,
this xenon atom possessed a fantastically large absorp-

tion capability or, shall we say, an enormous appetite for neutrons, stealing them away from the chain reaction. Fermi made an estimate of this "cross section" of the xenon atomic core and found it to be two million times the actual physical size of the core. He quipped, "The xenon nucleus is as big as an orange." Such was the speed with which the men worked that within about a day after the effect was noticed the mystery had been solved. Fortunately, there was enough leeway in the Hanford pile design to allow for overcoming this poisoning effect, and the machines were soon put into steady operation.

The enormous heat produced by the uranium fission would have quickly melted the pile unless the cooling water constantly carried the unwanted heat away. Special precautions were taken to hold up the discharge water to allow its radioactivity to die off before emptying the water back into the broad Columbia River. Even so, exhaustive tests were carried out to check up on the salmon in the river and to make sure that no one downstream would be injured by radioactivity.

For every ten U^{235} atoms which fissioned in the Hanford machine, approximately nine atoms of U^{238} were converted into neptunium which, in turn, formed plutonium. This new element would gradually build up inside the aluminum-jacketed slugs, but at the same time the radioactivity due to the split uranium atoms would increase. After cooking the slugs for several months the pile would be shut down and remote-control gadgets would discharge the "hot" slugs into baskets suspended under many feet of water. I will never forget the sight of these "hot" slugs glowing with an eerie blue light as they lay deep within the protecting shield of water.

If one were to consider all the fission debris from the big pile which accumulate in a year, the radioactivity would equal that emitted by thousands of *tons* of radium. Since even a fraction of an ounce of radium commands great respect, it is clear that the wartime project had to contend with an unprecedented radiation hazard. Time is a good healer in the case of fission products produced along with plutonium, so the hot slugs were allowed to cool for a month or so. Then all chemical processes designed to remove the small amount of plutonium from the large amount of uranium were engineered on a remote-control basis. These operations took place behind enormously thick concrete walls in what we called "The Canyon." Finally, the purified plutonium salt was carefully poured into stainless-steel, spillproof flasks. These were stored in special vaults until enough accumulated to warrant an armed-convoy shipment to the secret site where pure plutonium metal would be made.

It was nip and tuck whether or not Hanford would pay off before the parallel projects at Oak Ridge, namely, the U^{235} separation plants. A number of top scientists despaired of real success in separating U^{235} from its heavier twin. However, others were more optimistic even though undecided as to which road to take. Unlike the Plutonium Project which had a single aim—the nuclear reactor—the other project offered many avenues of approach. All depended upon the slight difference in weight between the two forms of uranium. Because the difference is so small and there was really no experience to serve as a guide, the experts were uncertain as to which "horse" they should back.

Actually, there were about six horses to reach the starting gate, all backed by at least a few experts. The odds involved for each seemed a reckless gamble, but scientists finally settled upon two as the best bets. We shall not describe these in as much detail as in the case of the Plutonium Project, for they are highly technical in nature. Moreover, the separation processes have little peacetime application as compared with the nuclear reactors.

One method involved processing of uranium gas. Ordinarily, the compound uranium hexafluoride is a solid. When exposed to air it gives off a not unpleasant odor (but a dangerous one) and fumes in a dense white cloud. Confined at twice atmospheric pressure and at a temperature somewhat below the boiling point of water, the solid turns to a colorless gas. This UF_6 gas is highly corrosive and must be kept in stainless-steel equipment. When this gas is pumped under pressure against a barrier consisting of very tiny holes, the gas which emerges on the other side of the partition is slightly enriched in U^{235}. The reason is that lighter uranium molecules move slightly faster than those consisting of U^{238}; hence the former have a slightly better chance of diffusing through the network of holes. Developing the proper barrier was quite a job, considering that it must contain hundreds of millions of uniform holes over an area of a few square inches. The slightest pinprick would short-circuit the barrier and render it useless.

Since the enrichment per stage is very slight, the gas has to be constantly recirculated under pressure. Thousands of stages are required in order to produce weapon-grade uranium. When the scientists had worked up pilot plants for separating uranium, a huge program of construction was undertaken under the code K-25. This was the gaseous diffusion project which culminated in the construction of a colossal U-shaped building, each wing of which is four hundred feet wide and half a mile long.

The other method involved electromagnetic separation of uranium along the lines which Dr. Dempster used in his atom-weighing device. At first it seemed incredible that such a method could ever be adapted to the large-scale production of weapon-grade uranium, but under Dr. E. O. Lawrence's direction improvements were made in magnetic separators so that construction was started on Y-12, the code name for the full-scale project. This plant was built at a cost of $350 million, which was $150 million cheaper than the K-25 plant and equal in cost to the Hanford reactors.

We mentioned that there originally were half a dozen methods of uranium separation considered. There is a fascinating and previously untold story behind the history of one of these methods. It concerns young Philip Abelson, whom we left with his discovery of neptunium. For some reason or other the nuclear chemist became interested in U^{235} separation, presumably because he acted as an advisor to the uranium steering committee back in 1941. Abelson seemed intuitively to pick the tough problems and so he was

right in form when he decided to rig up some equipment as a kind of one-man task force approach to
isotope separation. He had already licked the problem
of preparing pure uranium hexafluoride, so he turned
his attention upon what seemed an impossible problem. Technically known as thermal diffusion in liquids,
Abelson's method was simplicity itself, but there was
and still is no satisfactory theory for it. It consisted of
arranging three concentric pipes and maintaining two
of the surfaces at different temperatures. In June and
July of 1941 he constructed a thirty-six-foot column
and effected an appreciable separation of U^{235}—the
first major separation in the U.S.A.

Then Abelson made what was to be a major mistake;
he joined forces with the Navy and set up his equipment at the Naval Research Laboratory adjoining the
Potomac River south of the nation's capital. In 1943
Abelson expanded his one-man task force to a group
of five, but he remained the only Ph.D. on hand. Because he worked for the Navy, he was very quickly
"frozen out," to use his words, and could not find out
what was going on inside the Manhattan Project. He
did learn from the grapevine that no one was working
on his method and he also learned that things were
going rather slowly at Oak Ridge. So Phil persuaded
the Navy to advance more funds and he tried to get
more uranium for his research. Here he ran into a solid
wall, for the MED had a monopoly on this commodity.
The Navy was understandably reluctant about arguing
with a project that had the President's blessing, but
Abelson got the Navy to give him space at the Phila-
delphia Naval Shipyard. The war was at its peak, and

shipping losses and repairs were terrific. He found that he had priority 23—the end of the line at the shipyard. Undaunted by this, Abelson went out and made friends and influenced shipyard workers. By February of 1944 his pet project was in the pilot plant stage and looked promising although expensive.

In March of 1944 distress signals came from Oak Ridge. K-25 was in trouble and so was Y-12. Abelson had made an impression on Oak Ridge, when in July the summer before he had shipped Oak Ridge fifty pounds of 20 per cent enriched uranium. With this he levered out his uranium for his pilot plant and also impressed Edward Teller. The enigmatic Teller persuaded the Los Alamos laboratory director, J. Robert Oppenheimer, to contact General Groves about the Navy's upstart "quick and dirty" method of enriching uranium.

The worried General drove out to see Dr. Abelson and his equipment, wondering what he would find. The Corps of Engineers had committed a billion dollars on its approaches to producing bomb material. The Navy had spent a thousand times less. What if the Navy had come up with the much-feared "bathtub" method of producing bomb stuff? The War Department had frozen the Navy out of the picture, and you can imagine the General's apprehensions as he was driven through the gates of the Navy's Laboratory. What he saw did not seem impressive—just a lot of plumbing, rather small-scale stuff compared with Oak Ridge. Still, he thought, it was June 25, 1944. . . . General Patton was on the rampage in France and the war

might be over soon . . . he had better take Oppenheimer's advice.

General Groves didn't waste any time making a decision. On July 1, he authorized the S-50 project for
building a modest-sized plant to produce feed material
to perk up the lagging separation plant at Oak Ridge.
Actual construction costs amounted to only eight million dollars, and the plant was completed in the amaz-
ingly short time of seventy-five days. Things proceeded
to get gummed up as Groves refused to hire an independent operator for the plant and kept the construction firm on the job running the S-50 installation. The
important thing was that the plant did work, even
though it gobbled up vast quantities of steam—much
more than the K-25 plant on an even-Stephen basis. By
the time it was disassembled at the close of the war,
the plant had turned out many tons of enriched uranium. This was not fully enriched and could not be
used as bomb material, but it did prime the pump for
the Oak Ridge processes.

Looking back at the course of events, it is clear that
secrecy and Army-Navy hostility conspired to freeze
the "quick and dirty" Navy process out of the picture.
The S-50 plant could have been built a year earlier.
Even though it was expensive to operate because of its
high power-input requirements, its capital cost was
low. The delay in building S-50 could have proved
more valuable in the Plutonium Project than at Oak
Ridge. Consider, for example, the vexing problems
which Fermi and his colleagues faced in getting uranium and graphite pure enough to sustain the chain

reaction. Had the pile designers had access to even a relatively small amount of Abelson's enriched uranium, their worries would have vanished, Furthermore, by incorporating even a few per cent enriched uranium in the Hanford reactors, Fermi could have made much more compact and elegant plutonium producers. There is good reason to believe that the thirteen production reactors of the Atomic Energy Commission do employ enriched uranium.

Even though we may glance backward today and see how time could have been saved, those of us who lived through the hectic days of 1944 and 1945 were astonished at the speed with which the huge plants were erected. By the late spring of 1945 Hanford and Oak Ridge began to produce pounds of bombstuff. Metallurgists, working with techniques based on tiny samples of the precious material, carefully converted the product into shining metal.

The day was approaching when the bomb experts at Los Alamos, high on the mesa some thirty-five miles from Santa Fe, New Mexico, would put their theories to test.

chapter **4**

THE FIRST BOMB

Designing the processes and building the huge plants for producing bomb material was, in my opinion, the most time-consuming task which confronted the Manhattan Project. It is true that we had to perfect a bomb mechanism, but this task did not delay the payoff of the bomb project. Indeed, the weapons experts were ready to test the first bomb as soon as they got sufficient bomb stuff.

Had there been a speed-up in the production of bomb material so that we had enough of it in 1944 to test, I firmly believe that we could have tested our first weapon then. As it was, our first test of the Fat Man occurred in the desert of Alamogordo before dawn of July 16, 1945. But we were so confident of our ability to detonate a weapon that the first bomb exploded over Japan was of different design—called the Thin Man—a type never previously tested.

This is getting way ahead of the story, which centers on the Los Alamos laboratory and the development of the Thin Man and the Fat Man. The real task and the first order of business was to produce some ingredients for the atomic bomb, so the scientists tackled this job first and, gradually as problems were solved, the men became available for work on the bomb, itself. Theoretical work was launched in the summer of 1942 at the University of California under the guidance of thirty-eight-year-old J. Robert Oppenheimer. At the time he was a professor of physics at Berkeley and also at the California Institute of Technology at Pasadena. Known to almost all his friends simply as "Oppie," the young professor was famed for his insight into physical problems and his rare ability to work with others.

Oppenheimer gathered a small group of associates to skirmish with the problem of "critical size"—to try to estimate how much precious bomb stuff you would have to assemble to make an atomic bomb. Preliminary estimates ranged upward of five pounds or a sphere about the size of a billiard ball. But nobody really knew; much depended upon precise values for constants which remained to be determined by experiment. In fact, this was basically Fermi's philosophy toward the problem, namely, to learn more about neutrons, and if you could make a slow chain reaction, he reasoned you would know a great deal about making a fast one.

The spring of 1943 found Oppenheimer leading a small, somewhat bewildered group of theoreticians up a long winding road from Santa Fe, New Mexico. Their destination was Los Alamos, a tiny school community atop a high mesa where one could see the Sangre de Cristo Mountains. One could see the strange defile in the mountains where the snow etched a Christian cross against the rugged sides of the peaks. Here in the majestic solitude of New Mexico scientists banded together to see if a practicable bomb could be assembled. They started from scratch, and in their eagerness to get the job under way some of them practically stripped their own laboratories of their equipment. A complete cyclotron was uprooted from an eastern campus and shipped up the hill. This meant transporting it by truck up the hairpin turns on the dangerous single approach to the site. Some scientists and their wives, having survived the drive up the hill, seemed content to stay there rather than risk the downward trip.

Very shortly after the new laboratory was in business, Oppenheimer turned to the all-important task of recruiting scientists. It is a tribute to his administrative ability that he succeeded in attracting so many top-flight men to Los Alamos. Moreover, he managed to get the great Niels Bohr and such distinguished scientists as Sir James Chadwick and Dr. William Penney. It was proposed at one time that Oppenheimer be made a brigadier general and the Los Alamos staff be ranked accordingly. Oppenheimer initially was attracted to the idea, but his fellow scientists were appalled at the thought and persuaded him to keep the scientists in civilian garb.

I shall never forget my first trip to Los Alamos during the war. My thesis work had been on research which interested Oppenheimer, so we were more or less introduced before we met. This is one of the nice things about being a scientist. By means of your publications you become known to many people and develop friendships without actually meeting. However, I was not quite prepared for my first encounter with Oppenheimer when I walked through the Technical Area to his office on the second floor of the Army-barracks-type building. His secretary waved me into the inner office, and there I found the laboratory director pacing up and down. A full week's growth of beard plus his general scrawny appearance made him look like one of the traditional sourdough prospectors. I gazed in astonishment at his face. "Don't mind this," he said, indicating his face. "I've had a case of the measles and can't shave." He kept chain-smoking and talking, hooking his fingers into a large Mexican silver belt buckle—a fashion which much of Los Alamos imitated. I found him a most fascinating character and had I not known his profession I would have guessed that he might have been a great actor. His eyes, particularly, struck me as reflecting a sense of tragedy. This impressed me at the time and many times thereafter.

Our conversation was interrupted by a long-distance call from General Groves. Oppenheimer grimaced and answered the questions in rapid-fire fashion, completely sure of himself, but I sensed that he was deeply impressed with military rank—a feeling later fortified by my contacts with him in postwar Washington. The phone call concluded, Oppenheimer asked about Compton and others at the Met Lab when a booming concussion echoed into the room. These, I found later, were standard procedure at Los Alamos; they were dry runs on a detonating mechanism for the bomb. The booms came from canyons where a ton or more of TNT might be exploded to see how fast and how accurately explosions could be made. This, after all, would be the means by which the "assembly" of the bomb material would be made in the final weapon.

Two quite different methods were dreamed up by

the bomb experts, but before we discuss them we had better look at the all-important question of the "nuke" or critical mass inside the massive bomb mechanism.

Ordinary or natural uranium is, as we have seen, quite harmless for it will not, by itself, sustain a chain reaction. Only when it is embodied in an enormous matrix of some light element like graphite or heavy water does it sustain a slow chain reaction. Were this to be allowed to run out of control, it would not in general produce anything like an explosion. Heat would be produced and some inner parts of the reactor might melt, but it would not qualify as a bomb.

Enriched uranium or plutonium is quite different from ordinary uranium. Assemble too much of it in one place, and the chain reaction will automatically run away. Thus, it was rather important for the people at Oak Ridge and at Hanford to know how much was "enough" so that safety precautions could be taken. At Los Alamos the experts refined their calculations as to the size of the critical mass, but it was essential to have experimental measurements.

The man who headed up the "critical assembly" group was a good friend of mine. I knew Louis Slotin while an undergraduate at the University of Chicago and liked him very much for his pleasant manner and friendly advice. He was never too busy to help out a Ph.D. aspirant, and I remember that he gave me valuable pointers on making Geiger counters. On my visits to Los Alamos I used to stop by to see Slotin and give him the news of Chicago. He was a short, wiry youth with dark hair and soft sad eyes. Somehow or other, he always ended up doing jobs nobody else wanted. He never complained, and I respected the cheerful way that Slotin did dirty work.

Slotin had nerves of iron and he needed them for his critical experiments with the "nukes." Here is essentially what he did in making a critical assembly, or in "tickling the dragon's tail," as we called it. He would set up a table with a neutron counter and a rack. On the rack he would place two pieces of bomb stuff, each one being somewhat less than a critical amount. Then he would push the two pieces, often in the form of hemispheres the size of a split baseball, toward each other. As the gap narrowed between the pieces, he would measure the buildup of the chain reaction inside the assembly. He used a small source of neutrons to amplify the effect, rather than waiting for stray neutrons to come from cosmic rays or from the material itself. He determined the tempo of the buildup by listening to the clicks in an amplifier connected to the neutron counter and in watching a recorder trace out a jagged red line on a moving roll of graph paper.

As the hemispheres came closer and closer, more and more of the neutrons would tend to be caught within the bomb stuff and fewer would be lost through the narrowing air gap. The chain reaction would build up, and, just before it was ready to rip, Slotin would calmly stop the experiment, measure the separation and deduce just how big the critical mass was. He grew quite adept at the experiment for he repeated it fifty times or more. His nonchalance amazed Fermi who once warned him, "Keep doing that experiment that way and you'll be dead within a year." Some of

Slotin's colleagues tried to get him to build in automatic safety devices, like powerful springs, which could be triggered to hurl the two hemispheres apart when the neutrons built up too fast. He turned aside this suggestion with this retort: "If I have to depend upon safety devices I am sure to have an accident."

Slotin was asked to repeat the experiment "just one more time" to demonstrate the technique to others in the laboratory. So he gathered the group of six people behind him in the sunlit room where he did his work. One man, Dr. Alvin Graves, had his hand almost on his shoulder as Slotin proceeded to demonstrate his technique. He used two hemispheres that he had worked with before and holding a screwdriver he moved the two pieces of bomb material together to form a "nuke" or nuclear core. Slowly, at first, then more quickly the counters clicked away and the red line moved upward on the white paper chart.

Suddenly the counters screamed and the red ink indicators swung off scale. There had been an accident! The chain reaction was running away. Almost as if by reflex action Slotin hurled himself forward and tore the reacting mass apart with his bare hands. The others gasped and, turning around, Slotin, his face whitely reflecting his terror, motioned them to leave the room.

Slotin telephoned the hospital and said that there had been an accident. Then he telephoned his close friend, Phil Morrison. He was nauseated but, always the true scientist, paused in the hallway and drew a pencil sketch of the room and marked everyone's position, putting a big X for himself. Then he scribbled the time, 3:20 P.M., and hustled the group off to the hospital, all of them jamming into two jeeps.

The big question in the mind of everyone was: how much dose did Slotin get? The neutrons and X rays which flashed through his body before he tore the assembly apart caused biological damage to his body. This we measure in certain units—called roentgens or r-units. A total of about 400 r over the entire body is considered the lethal amount for most people. This deadly amount does not produce immediate effect but takes time . . . weeks . . . or days . . . depending on the dose.

Phil Morrison, gifted theoretical physicist, worked feverishly to reconstruct the accident and to learn how serious was his friend's plight. Slotin's very blood had been made radioactive by the burst of neutrons which riddled his body, and a small sample of his blood gave a clue to the dose. Of course, Slotin was hospitalized and became ill rather soon, but during the first few days he was cheerful and would ask when visited by Morrison, "Well, what's the dose?" Nobody really knew and it took a long time to find out. Before they did, the tide had changed in Slotin's reaction to the radiation. His differential blood cell count told the story—a picture so hopeless that the attending Army nurse, hardened to hospital routine, broke down and sobbed when she saw the results.

Slotin had been most severely irradiated around the hands and arms. These parts of his pain-ridden body swelled grotesquely and the skin sloughed off. The nation's best doctors were flown to the Army hospital at Los Alamos but they could do little for the weakening patient. Nor could we do much more today.

Technicians strung a telephone connection into the bare hospital room and Slotin talked with his mother in Winnipeg, Canada. The next day, his parents were flown to New Mexico by special Army plane, and they stayed at their son's bedside until he breathed his last. The end came early on the morning of the ninth day after the accident.

The man who stood behind Slotin, Dr. Graves, was severely injured by the accident but he recovered and went on to become associate director of Los Alamos in the postwar period. He had this to say of Slotin: "I can perhaps tell you as much about his personality and character as I could in very many words if I merely quote to you his first statement when we were alone together in the hospital room. He said, 'I'm sorry I got you into this. I am afraid that I have less than a fifty-fifty chance of living. I hope you do better than that.'"

Slotin was not destined to be a great or a famous man. He was one of the many scientists who worked devotedly and unselfishly throughout the war. The young scientist gave his life, just as did many of his comrades in arms.

Slotin's experiment was outlawed at Los Alamos. With the development of television and remote-control gadgetry, it became possible to do the critical assembly operations with no one within a quarter of a mile. White-coated technicians, principally women, control the assembly and make all their observations without the slightest danger to themselves.

The trick in going from Slotin's experiment to the actual firing of an A-bomb is to make the assembly as rapidly as possible—and, of course, not to be close by. Moreover, the assembly should be rigged to stay together long enough for the chain reaction to split an appreciable number of the fissionable atoms.

A good many ideas were kicked around at Los Alamos as to how to accomplish this trick. Clearly, the rapid assembly of the subcritical pieces into a chain reacting "nuke" required some type of explosive charge. An obvious method was to construct a gun type of device consisting of a long gun barrel, unusual in that it would be closed at both ends. At one end one would imbed a "target" of bomb stuff but not quite enough to be critical, while at the other end of the barrel one would fit in a "projectile" of U^{235}, again not quite a critical amount. Behind this projectile one could place a propellant. This straightforward gun-type weapon was developed at Los Alamos and was nicknamed "the Thin Man."

The British sent to Los Alamos not only their best nuclear experts but, just as important, they gave us explosives specialists like Sir William Taylor and Dr. William Penney. These men were absolutely essential to the development of the bomb for it involved much work with ordnance. In the case of the Thin Man, the approach was not too sophisticated and there was little doubt that the gadget would work. However, it was looked upon as a brute force approach and one which would not be very efficient in the use of the precious bomb stuff.

Rather than describe the Thin Man in more detail, we shall proceed to another type of bomb design, namely, the Fat Man. This was a much more elegant and imaginative approach to making a nuclear weapon but it was also a greater adventure into the unknown. Many scientists doubted that it would ever work out, but Oppenheimer was confident that it would pay off. It involved a principle which could be summed up in one word, "implosion." This word, itself, was classified secret until almost six years after Hiroshima and Nagasaki. Then it startled the atomic scientists for it appeared in the daily newpapers on March 13, 1951. "Atom Bomb Secret Described in Court" was the lead in the *New York Times* article which described the trial of twenty-nine-year-old David Greenglass, a former Army sergeant, who had worked as foreman of a machine shop at Los Alamos.

Young David Greenglass admitted passing on to a Soviet agent the details of an "implosion device" for accomplishing a nuclear reaction in a plutonium sphere. Inasmuch as the Soviets received detailed sketches of the device, as well as lengthy explanatory texts from Dr. Klaus Fuchs, the implosion gadget or Fat Man can hardly be much of a secret. I shall adhere very closely to Greenglass' court testimony in describing it.

Starting at the very center of the bomb, we have the "nuke"—the hollow plutonium sphere, probably no larger than a baseball, and nestled in the cavity there was a beryllium sphere which provided a source of neutrons. Around the plutonium "nuke" there was fitted together a huge sphere composed of thirty-six chunks or prisms of high explosive, all neatly machined to form a solid sphere. Each of the thirty-six prisms contained two detonators (one would be enough, but a spare was added for safety), and these were linked together in a firing circuit. This was the anatomy of the Fat Man as revealed by David Greenglass.

We can understand its mechanism if we start from the outside and work our way in toward the "nuke" buried in the center, as Oppenheimer put it, like a diamond in an enormous wad of cotton. If all the detonators fire simultaneously, and we mean that precisely, then the instantaneous explosion of more than a ton of high explosive produces a tremendous blast. Part of the blast wave from each prism will focus inward and converge upon the buried "nuke." All the converging blast waves, arriving precisely at the same time, squeeze the hollow plutonium sphere and cause it to collapse around the beryllium core as though it were a ping-pong ball. Undeterred, the implosion wave presses inward and squashes the plutonium into an overcritical mass. The nuclear chain reaction ignites under the blowtorch effect of the neutron source. Within one-millionth of one second the chain reaction races to completion. What was once a cool, shining metal sphere is transformed into a raging multimillion degree hot gas. This is an atomic explosion.

It all sounds rather easy, but the timing of events in this gadget called for unprecedented precision. One had to be positive that all the high-explosive lenses would explode at exactly the same time. The lens design had to be worked out in exquisite detail to focus the blast wave in the same way that a piece of glass may be ground to focus light. Except that the high-explosive lenses had to be tested in the field—that explains the booms which I heard when in Oppenheimer's office.

If the implosion got off to a bad start and the shock waves did not arrive at the center simultaneously, then the gadget would be lopsided and would blow itself apart. Rather than producing a real atomic explosion, it might "fizzle." In fact, the probability of a fizzle was a worry right up to the time of the first test at Alamogordo, so much so that a great U.S. engineering firm was ordered to make the largest steel shell on record. Known as "Dumbo," it was designed to enclose the test bomb and to confine the partially exploded material in the event of a dud or fizzle. It proved to be a nuisance so it was not used, and later was taken out in the desert and blown apart with a huge stack of TNT.

On my periodic visits to Los Alamos in 1945, before the first test, I found varying degrees of "optimism" about the chances for the bomb working. I can sum it up by saying that there was little doubt that an atomic explosion could be made; the only question was "How big a bang?" Based purely upon Professor Einstein's yardstick, a single pound of bomb stuff could produce the equivalent blast of nine thousand tons of TNT, *provided* every single uranium atom fissioned in the chain reaction. In other words, provided that the bomb-makers hit a hundred per cent efficiency. This, of course, was impossible but they had some confidence that the first bomb would yield a blast equal to ten thousand tons of TNT. Or, to use the jargon of Los Alamos, it would be at least a 10-kiloton (kt) bomb.

It was decided that the Fat Man would be tested in the desert or badlands of New Mexico about two hundred miles south of Los Alamos. The date: Monday, July 16, 1945; the time: 3:30 A.M. Sunday evening, before sunset, a long caravan of cars and trucks wound down the road from Los Alamos headed south. Through the darkness the heavily guarded convoy rolled toward the test site, arriving there shortly before 2 A.M. The scientists, engineers and visiting fireman deployed themselves according to plan. Nearest to the test tower were the men at the control revetment, some nine miles from Ground Zero. Most observers took their stations twenty miles away, stretching out on the still warm sand to rest until H-hour.

At 2:30 A.M. it was announced that the test would be postponed until 5:30. The sleepless men began to wonder if the weather would clear; rain would be disastrous, since it would impose a severe threat of radioactive contamination to the area.

At 5:25 A.M. the darkness of the sky was illuminated by the flash from a warning rocket. Five minutes to go. The automatic controls would now take over. 5:29 another rocket signalled one more minute . . . then over the radio came the count . . . the seconds were ticked off by Dr. S. K. Allison, and finally the moment arrived.

The desert was flooded with light which splashed off the mountains forty miles away. Quickly the scientists peered through bits of dark-colored glass to see the spectacle. In a brief split second the point of light expanded, rolling out over the flat, sandy soil, forming a helmet-shaped glowing mass. The burst of piercing daylight flickered out and the bomb-makers watched in awe the grotesque gymnastics of the still-hot fireball as it rose slowly above the earth's surface and then more quickly shot upward, forming the now too familiar mushroom cloud.

Exactly one hundred seconds later the shock wave of the blast reached the observers sprawled out on the ground. All but Fermi, for he stood up and calmly dropped small bits of paper to the ground . . . an unforgettable silhouette of a man impatient to know the answer . . . he had on the spur of the moment devised his own method for measuring the blast.

"It works," was the shout sent up as the other scientists got to their feet. Ernest Lawrence grabbed Charles Thomas, now president of Monsanto Chemical Company, and jumped up and down, hollering with the others, "It works!" The scientists cavorted on the desert sands, making inarticulate sounds and slapping each other on the back. Even the reserved Chadwick was rocked with a backslap, but he maintained his taciturnity.

Nature had yielded up its most tightly bound secret to man's prying grasp. A single sphere of plutonium no larger than a baseball could now equal the violence of tens of thousands of tons of TNT. The tall iron test tower had been vaporized, leaving behind only broken stubs imbedded in shattered concrete. The desert floor was dished out as though depressed by an enormous fist, and this crater was covered with a glassy greenish-hued surface. The crusty vitrified sand, turned to glass by the bomb's flame, crunched underfoot and glistened in the redness of the rising sun. I have on my desk a sample of this green-glazed soil along with a piece of iron sawed from the remains of the test tower. It's safe now, a decade later, but for a long time I kept the iron sample inside a lead box to protect against its radioactivity.

The Alamogordo test was code named *TRINITY*. A most appropriate or a most vulgar designation, depending upon your point of view! The world's first nuclear detonation came at a time when President Truman was meeting with Josef Stalin at Potsdam. In fact, the President received a message from Secretary of War Henry L. Stimson, reading: "Babies satisfactorily born." The next day as the Potsdam Conference was opened, Mr. Stimson personally briefed the President on the results of the Trinity test. On July 24, Mr. Truman sauntered to one end of the conference room and mentioned to Stalin the existence of the "new weapon of unusual destructive force," but the Russian leader gave no indication of being impressed, other than that he was glad to hear of the development and hoped that the bomb would be used against Japan. Stalin also urged that the new weapon development be kept secret.

The decision to use the bomb against Japan ranks as one of the most fateful acts of our government. In reviewing the steps which led to our dropping A-bombs on Japan, it is well to remember that the United States was at war and decisions were made by a few officials operating in great secrecy. That is to say, the decision was scarcely democratic in the sense that information was made available to the public and the decision process made in the light of day. In my view the tragic mistake which the United States made in deciding to use the weapon derived in part from the internal secrecy, i.e., within the War Department and executive offices, which allowed individuals to have access to fragmentary data about the war situation.

While I personally believe that the decision to use the bomb will rank as one of the greatest errors in judgment on the part of U.S. officials, I hasten to add that it was not made on the basis of snap judgment. It was a deliberate and calculated decision. This, to me, makes the mistake all the more tragic.

Both Mr. Truman and Mr. Stimson have given their account of the decision to use the bomb. Additionally, the late Dr. Karl T. Compton reviewed the decision in the light of what might have happened if we had not used the bomb. Mr. Stimson went to the White House on April 25, 1945, to brief the new President upon the atomic project. He took General Groves with him to present a status report and prospectus for the bomb development. General Groves stated that the bomb would probably be a reality within four months. The Secretary of War emphasized the revolutionary nature of the weapon as is illustrated by his published memorandum in which he stated: "The world in its present state of moral advancement compared with its technical development would be eventually at the mercy of such a weapon. In other words, modern civilization might be completely destroyed."

After this presidential briefing, a select committee was organized to advise the President of the implications which the new weapon might have for the world. Secretary Stimson headed this group, which included: George L. Harrison, president of the New York Life Insurance Company; James F. Byrnes; Ralph A. Bard, Undersecretary of the Navy; William L. Clayton, Assistant Secretary of State; Dr. Vannevar Bush; Dr. Karl T. Compton and Dr. James B. Conant. This committee was assisted in its work by a Scientific Panel composed of Arthur H. Compton, Enrico Fermi, E. O. Lawrence and J. Robert Oppenheimer.

This committee and its advisory panel met on May 31, 1945, to give its recommendations on the use of the weapon. Their conclusions were relayed to the White House the next day as Mr. Truman records in his *Memoirs* (Vol. I—*Year of Decisions*):

It was their recommendation that the bomb be used against the enemy as soon as it could be done. They recommended further that it should be used without specific warning and against a target that would clearly show its devastating strength. I had realized, of course, that an atomic bomb explosion would inflict damage and casualties beyond imagination. On the other hand, the scientific advisors of the committee reported that, "We can propose no technical demonstration likely to bring an end to the war; we see no acceptable alternative to direct military use."

Here, clearly, was the first spectacular confluence of science and national affairs. Scientists were being asked to give their advice on matters of immense military and international significance. Moreover, these scientists were asked to give advice with respect to the use of a weapon relative to its ending the war. This very definitely implied evaluation of the over-all military situation. And, specifically, matters narrowed down to the military situation in the beleaguered home islands of Japan. How badly had Japanese cities been hit by the TNT and fire-bombing? How much had the interdiction of raw materials from the mainland and island empire hurt Japanese industry? How long could the Japanese people stand up under the pommeling of ceaseless air attack? We now know the answer in the form of an excellent analysis made by the U.S. Strategic Bombing Survey titled *Japan's Struggle to End the War*—a report which made it all too clear that Japan was already on her knees when the first A-bomb was dropped. This, you may argue, was a *post facto* appraisal of the true situation in Japan and hardly applicable to the situation as of May 31, 1945. However, aerial photoreconnaissance of Japan revealed to Army Air Corps Intelligence the true state of affairs as of that date. Unfortunately, either this information did not filter up to Generals Arnold and Marshall or they did not take it seriously. Yet in a Memorandum for the President (July 2, 1945) the Secretary of War summed up Japan's plight: ". . . Japan has no allies. Her navy is nearly destroyed and she is vulnerable to a surface and underwater blockade which can deprive her of sufficient food and supplies for her population. She is terribly vulnerable to our concentrated air attack upon her crowded cities, industrial and food resources. . . ."

In the face of these facts, President Truman authorized the use of the bomb against Japan. He did not duck the responsibility, for in his *Memoirs* he writes: "The final decision of where and when to use the atomic bomb was up to me. Let there be no mistake about it. I regarded the bomb as a military weapon and never had any doubt that it should be used."

Four cities were selected as targets for man's new creation: Hiroshima, Kokura, Nagasaki and Niigata, in order of strategic priority. General Arnold had wanted Kyoto to be included, but Mr. Stimson wisely struck that cultural center off the list.

The world knows and I shall not retell the story of Hiroshima and Nagasaki. But there is a dramatic and largely untold story of a secret debate and report, which took place before Hiroshima and even before Alamogordo, which I shall report in some detail. In my opinion it ranks as a prime example of clear-headed thinking by scientists in the area of world affairs, and, even in the harsh light of a decade later, it emerges as prophetic and significant.

Leader of the debate and organizer of the report was Dr. James Franck, one of the most loved scientists in this country. Soft-voiced and gentle-mannered Professor Franck worked on the Manhattan Project during the war. During the spring of 1945 he became worried about the problems which would be broken out into the open by the A-bomb and headed up a secret task force of three chemists, three physicists and a lone biologist; they called themselves a "Committee on Social and Political Implications." These men, debating the bomb in the guarded rooms on the University of Chicago campus, were not the first to consider the consequences of unlocking atomic energy. But when they formulated their report on June 11, 1945, the atmosphere was somewhat different from what it had been earlier. Germany had been vanquished and we were no longer in a race to get the bomb. The war in the Pacific was progressing favorably and brought into focus the use of the A-bomb against Japan. The Franck Report was submitted to the Secretary of War and represented a dissenting voice, arguing against the direct military use of the new weapon, which, incidentally, it pinpointed as equal to twenty thousand tons of TNT.

In an almost apologetic tone, the report began: ". . . The scientists on this Project do not presume to speak authoritatively on problems of national and international policy. However, we found ourselves, by the force of events, during the last five years, in the position of a small group of citizens cognizant of a grave danger for the safety of this country as well as for the future of all other nations, of which mankind is unaware." The report warned against the false hope that the bomb might be kept secret, pointing out that it would only be a few years before other countries had the selfsame weapon. It urged extreme caution in considering the use of the new weapon, emphasizing that after the war international control of the atom would be of paramount importance and that the United States might not appear in a favorable light if it used the bomb indiscriminately. Fearing a "wave of horror and repulsion sweeping over the rest of the world," the report concluded: "A demonstration of the new weapon might best be made, before the eyes of representatives of all the United Nations, on the desert or a barren island." Then, it was argued, America could say to the world, "You see what sort of weapon we had but did not use. We are ready to renounce its use in the future if other nations join us in this renunciation and agree to the establishment of an efficient international control."

The Franck Report acknowledged the problem of weighing the loss of American life should the war in the Pacific be protracted. This is a point on which Dr. Karl T. Compton made his case when he viewed with horror the sacrifice of hundreds of thousands of Americans on the rocky shores of Japan. It is true that General Douglas MacArthur was slated to command an invasion force late in the fall of 1945; in fact, dress rehearsals for that invasion were already under way when the A-bomb was dropped. It is equally true that Japan would probably have mustered sufficient strength to exact a high toll from the invading force. But that an invasion was necessary is quite another point. All signs pointed to Japan as a textbook case for strategic bombing, and to argue that the A-bomb had to be used in order to save lives lost in an invasion is to bow down before the judgments of TNT-minded generals, too suddenly presented with the power of extraordinary weapons.

The fact remains that our top leaders failed to recognize the unconventional attributes of the new bomb and, what is worse, that some upper-crust scientists collaborated with the military in their unimaginative use of the bomb. A nation, blessed with the ingenuity which birthed atomic energy, found itself led by officials who plodded along in the age-old rut of war. Historians will duly record that man in his conquest of the atom used his new-found power to destroy his fellow man.

chapter 5

URANIUM AND STOCKPILE

The Franck Report was more than an advisory on the non-use of the new bomb. It surveyed the future of atomic energy in the postwar period and tried to discern how important the atom might be in peacetime. Thus, even before Hiroshima, scientists had turned their thoughts to the ways of peace. Indeed, quite a few scientists believed deeply that the A-bomb, itself, would prove a powerful force for peace. Man, they reasoned, would at last have to put an end to the dreadful succession of wars which have marked recorded history. Now the penalties for going to war would be too great for an aggressor nation to risk.

Scientists like Szilard and Franck were not sublime optimists. They had their feet on the ground and knew that man would not mend his ways overnight. Furthermore, they realized that, although the scientists could grasp the new dimension of this new force, the laymen and statesmen would take years to grasp its significance. During this period of gradual enlightenment, the world would most certainly be plunged into a fearful arms race. Nations might want to sit at international conference tables to discuss peace, but they would feel naked and insecure, unless they came to the conference backed up by the might of new arms, so that they could negotiate as equals. These thoughts were in the mind of men like Szilard long before the A-bomb was proof-tested.

I remember Leo Szilard pacing up and down the third-floor corridor of Eckart Hall on the Chicago campus. Back and forth he would pace like a restless bear. He and Edward Teller used to hold long conversations in this free-wheeling style, and I would often glance up from my office desk and see them pass by, engrossed in argument. One day in March, 1945, Szilard had a bright idea: he would put down his thoughts in orderly fashion and address a letter to President Roosevelt, outlining his views of things to come in the postwar period.

Later, Szilard told me that in this case he decided "to be a good boy and go through channels," which was, to say the least, unorthodox procedure for the Hungarian-born scientist. He went to the Project Director, Arthur Compton, and outlined his plan, expecting that Compton would discourage him. On the contrary, he was given the green light, and Szilard set about making his forecast of the future. He completed his self-assigned task one afternoon in April, the very moment when the radio brought the news of the President's death.

Szilard's memorandum to Roosevelt was dispatched nonetheless and stands as a most remarkable (but little known) prophecy. Directing attention to the 1945 model bombs, he wrote: "These bombs will be much less powerful than the ones we now know could be made, and in all likelihood will be made later; yet the first bomb that is detonated over Japan will be spectacular enough to start a race in atomic armaments between us and other nations."

Russia, he maintained, would put high priority on

uranium work and would break our atomic monopoly within a few years. "For a few years," Szilard wrote, ". . . we shall almost certainly be ahead of Russia. But even if we assume that we could keep ahead of her in this development all the time, this may neither offer us protection from attack nor give us substantial advantage in case of war." Szilard summed it up: "The strong position of the United States in the world in the past thirty years has been due to the fact that the U.S. could out-produce every other country in heavy armaments. The existence of the atomic bomb means the end of the strong position of the United States in this respect."

Great emphasis was placed upon international control of atomic energy. Szilard foresaw an era of atomic abundance in which the basic materials of nuclear weapons would be mass-produced. In fact, he later told a Senate committee that twenty tons of bomb stuff might be easily produced. Thus, he was jumping over the pitifully small supplies on hand at the end of the war to the day when bomb material would be available in vastly greater supply.

Following the end of the war Congress debated the proper framework for the postwar development of atomic energy. The chief issue to be decided was whether the atom would continue under military control or be placed under new management. A valiant group of young scientists championed the cause of civilian control, and a number of ivory tower escapees invaded Washington, D.C., to lobby for an Atomic Energy Act of their own liking. Politically wise observers smiled at this scientific lobby, which violated all the rules, and muttered that it wouldn't work. But the scientists found a champion in Connecticut's Senator Brien McMahon.

Mr. Atom, as the astute Senator became known, closeted himself with some nuclear physicists and literally absorbed nuclear knowledge preparatory to leading the fight on Capitol Hill for a civilian atomic agency. Senator McMahon very wisely arranged for there to be public hearings on a bill of his own design. Scientists, engineers and government officials were called before a special group of Congressmen to give their views on the atom. These out-of-print hearings still rank as a unique exposition of all phases of atomic energy and represent a true *Operation Candor*. Never again was the atom to be so thoroughly examined in public.

On August 1 of 1946 the Atomic Energy Act or McMahon Act became law, and a civilian Atomic Energy Commission was duly established. A five-member Commission was set up to direct the activities of the new agency, and President Truman designated these men late in 1946. Former TVA czar David Lilienthal was named chairman, while scientist Robert F. Bacher, OPA official Sumner Pike, Admiral Lewis L. Strauss and Pulitzer prizeman W. W. Waymack rounded out the Commission. They met for the first time on November 13, 1946, to consider their inheritance from the Manhattan Engineer District. All of the Manhattan facilities were transferred to the AEC as of the last day of 1946.

This transfer from MED to AEC saw the control of atomic energy taken from General Leslie Groves and handed over to David Lilienthal. The two men were not on friendly terms—to put it mildly—and Lilienthal refused to have anything to do with the General. This was most unfortunate since General Groves was by this time a most unhappy and a rather lonely figure in Washington. He had managed to irritate some outstanding scientists and had stomped the country giving speeches which could properly be labeled "I did it alone." It happened that I was an advisor to the War Department General Staff at the time, and I used to be number two man, following Groves, who always gave the lead-off lecture. Driving back from military bases with the General, I would listen to his lament as he detailed his woes. He felt that he was not given proper credit for his work during the war. Moreover, the General managed to irritate many of his fellow star-bearing officers. At least six generals in the Pentagon disliked Groves so much that they went to considerable lengths to prepare a sharp bed of thorns for him there. To top matters off, Groves found that the new AEC chief never once asked his advice on anything. General Groves later stated ". . . Mr. Lilienthal had made it very plain that he wanted no advice of any kind from me. He wanted nothing whatsoever to do with me. He thought that I was the lowest kind of human being, and he was not going to get anything from me." This was humiliating, and the General made things difficult for Lilienthal.

Lilienthal, however, had many woes. As the top man of TVA, he became a target for Congressional sharpshooting so that it was natural for target practice to continue after Lilienthal took over the atomic project. Lilienthal's confirmation as chairman of the AEC was the occasion for subjecting him to a prolonged and agonizing grilling. The result was that, although he came through the ordeal, he was seared by the investigation so that he became a very conservative leader for the AEC. The ex-TVA chief not only had enemies on Capitol Hill and in the Pentagon, but in addition was opposed by Admiral Lewis L. Strauss, his fellow Commissioner.

When the AEC took stock of its MED property it became apparent that the year and a half lapse of time between the end of the war and the beginning of the civilian atomic agency had put atomic production into the doldrums. The huge plutonium production plants on the Columbia River were sputtering in disrepair. Uranium separation plants were not at top-notch performance. Los Alamos scientists were discouraged about the future. Moreover, world affairs had taken a severe turn for the worse. The split world was made more terrible by the reality of the split atom.

Something had to be done about producing more bomb stuff and developing better weapons.

Vast quantities of uranium would be required for a stepped-up atomic program. The Atomic Energy Commission looked into its inventories of the all-important ore and then launched an ambitious two-pronged attack on solving the uranium deficit.

During the war and up to the time the AEC began operations, the two principal sources of uranium were the Eldorado Mine on the shore of Great Bear Lake in Canada and the fabulous Shinkolobwe Mine deep in the heart of the Belgian Congo. As a matter of fact, prior to the war there were only four major sources of uranium ore. In addition to the two mentioned, there was the oldest producing mine—the Joachimsthal mines on the former German-Czechoslovakian border —which has been in operation for about a century and the Colorado Plateau deposits in this country.

The Joachimsthal deposits were mined originally as a source of uranium to be used in coloring ceramics. Then, with Madame and Pierre Curie's work on radium, they became important as a source of radium and were worked extensively since it takes three million pounds of uranium to yield a single pound of radium. It is understood that the Soviets have exploited the Czechoslovakian ores by using tens of thousands of slave laborers during recent years.

Gilbert A. LaBine, a rugged Canadian prospector, first spotted the outcroppings of the Great Bear Lake uranium beds north of the Arctic Circle in the year of the Great Crash on Wall Street. However, his buried treasure was tucked away in the Arctic 1600 miles from the nearest railhead. Motivated largely because of a need to produce cheap radium and break the sky-high monopoly price of the Belgian Syndicate, LaBine overcame his mining and transportation difficulties and engaged the Belgians in a price war which ultimately sent the market for radium plummeting down to twenty-five thousand dollars per gram, or more than three times less than its monopoly price. Square-jawed LaBine kept his mine in operation right up to the outbreak of World War II when his principal markets in Europe were cut off; then he closed down operations.

He was much surprised two years later when the Canadian government stepped in and presented him with a huge order for uranium oxide, the blackish heavy ore which had previously been of value only in terms of its radium content. Throughout the war the Great Bear mines kept producing, and the ore was transported by river boat southward. Many transfers from lake vessels to trucks to river boats were needed to bring the valuable mineral to a railhead north of Edmonton, and work was restricted to the scant three months when the summer sun thawed the frozen lakes and rivers.

Contrasting with the Arctic origin of Great Bear uranium, the bulk of the U.S. imports during the war came from the steaming tropics of the Belgian Congo where natives dug lustrous pitchblende from surface outcroppings of the Shinkolobwe Mines. The fabulous mother lode of uranium had been discovered by a Major Sharp during World War I when he stumbled upon the yellow-greenish outcroppings. Actually, he had been prospecting for copper and silver when he hit the uranium jackpot—although it probably didn't seem like a jackpot at the time, since uranium was not much in demand. By 1921 Union Minière du Haut-Katanga worked the mines for their radium product and captured a monopoly which was not broken until Gilbert LaBine struck it rich on the barren shores of Great Bear Lake. Like the Canadian mine, Shinkolobwe was shut down after the start of World War II.

Belgian stockpiles of uranium ore worried Leo Szilard when it became apparent to him that Hitler might invade the Lowlands following his push eastward through Poland. Der Fuehrer had clamped an embargo on all uranium from Czechoslovakia, and Szilard feared that he would try to scoop up the Belgian ore, too. The rotund, fast-traveling physicist took steps to keep the uranium out of Hitler's clutches.

When the Manhattan Engineer District negotiated with the Belgian government-in-exile to reopen the Shinkolobwe Mines, Colonel K. D. Nichols, who was number two man in the Project, learned to his surprise that there were twelve hundred tons of hand-picked, high-grade ore stockpiled in a warehouse on Staten Island. This bonanza formed the basis for early uranium research in the Project as well as for bomb production. Thereafter, a steady procession of ships crossed the Atlantic with a secret cargo—dirty and seemingly worthless uranium oxide. Wartime shipments consisted of ore assaying 50 to 65 per cent pure, selected from surface dumps, augmented later by pitchblende mined during 1943 and 1944. Forty-two ships set out across the submarine-infested Atlantic, and fortunately only two of them were sunk. By the end of the war the flow of precious uranium to Oak Ridge, Tennessee, had swollen to at least ten thousand tons. Of this amount only a trickle came from native U.S. deposits on the Colorado Plateau.

AEC officials were disturbed that the U.S. should have to depend upon imports for almost all its uranium feed material for atomic plants and began encouraging exploration for the valuable ore within our borders. Meanwhile, the AEC continued to increase its imports from Canada and Africa and to encourage world-wide exploration for workable beds of uraniferous ore. But its uranium requirements, reckoned by today's standards, were quite modest, and it was not until Senator Brien McMahon sparked a tremendous expansion of atomic production facilities that the heat was really put on for procurement of uranium. The expansion of plants to produce bomb material came in three successive waves which overlapped each other, one starting before the other finished. The first wave included a program for increased production at Oak Ridge and Hanford; this was a relatively modest swell. Wave number two was more impressive and included new billion-dollar sites which were enlarged as the final and just completed expansion was authorized.

The Senator from Connecticut took to the floor of the Senate in mid-September of 1951 to urge an all-out crash program on atomic arms. He foresaw an atomic Army, Navy and Air Force, armed with a diversified inventory of nuclear weapons, and he proposed a vast increase in the supply of bomb stuff to provide these weapons. It was in this impassioned speech that the Senator, soon to die of cancer, revealed that an atomic bomb could be made for less than the cost of an Army tank. Taking the unit cost of a Walker Bulldog at $150,-000, this allows one to make some estimate, admittedly rough, of how much bomb stuff is required for an A-bomb. We need a few more figures to work this out but we can estimate that the valuable bomb stuff constitutes two-thirds of the bomb cost and that the "nuke" material costs ten thousand dollars per pound. Simple arithmetic puts the weight of the "nuke" at ten pounds. This would correspond to a sphere about the size of a baseball. Such a "nuke" would have a maximum destructive force equal to ninety thousand tons of TNT, but in practice only a fraction of this total would be attainable. In fact, one of the main objectives of weapon development, discussed in the next chapter, was and still is the design of weapons so that more explosive force can be squeezed out of a "nuke."

I have a very definite purpose in making this brief excursion into the anatomy of nuclear weapons; namely, to show the relation between the "nuke" and the stockpile. The "nuke" is fabricated of almost pure U^{235} or plutonium. Let's focus attention upon U^{235} and its separation in the huge Oak Ridge plants or in the newer installations at Paducah, Kentucky, and those near Portsmouth, Ohio. The feed material for these plants is originally a heavy yellow paste—a uranium compound, which is converted into uranium hexafluoride, the toxic gas which we discussed earlier. Natural uranium contains only seven-tenths of one per cent U^{235}, but not all this can be extracted in the Oak Ridge type plants. Let's assume that one U^{235} atom out of every three hundred uranium atoms can be separated. Now we can work backward from Senator McMahon's assertion about the price of an A-bomb and our arithmetic regarding the "nuke." To produce one of McMahon's bombs would require an input at Oak Ridge of three thousand pounds of pure uranium. Thus, as a rough rule of thumb we can say that a ton of natural uranium equals one small A-bomb. Obviously, a bigger A-bomb would require more tons of input or feed material at Oak Ridge.

We are now in a position to look more critically at the matter of uranium supply. Senator McMahon's

huge expansion of atomic production facilities envisaged bomb production in the thousands and tens
of thousands. In point of fact, Dr. John Dunning, who
did pioneer work on the atom at Columbia University,
specifically referred to possible "bomb production in
the tens of thousands" shortly after Senator McMahon
made his famous speech. The production of such numbers of A-bombs would require a minimum procurement of tens of thousands of tons of pure uranium and,
actually, much more to stock the "pipelines" at our
atomic factories.

Demand for tens of thousands of tons of pure uranium stimulated a global search for new sources of the
precious ore. Naturally, the United States took pains
to secure the output of the Belgian Congo mines. The
surface deposits petered out and exploitation of shaft-
mining was necessary, but even so the rich pay dirt of
prewar and war years was not to be found. Still, the
residual deep-lying ore was rich as compared with ore
deposits in other countries. But the U.S. looked elsewhere for more uranium and found it in Africa in a
most unexpected place.

South Africa is famous for its gold and diamond
mines. For example, it is estimated that the gold reserves there amount to more than twelve billion dollars.
In the course of mining the gold ore, the pay dirt is
chemically processed and the gold removed from a
soupy slime. This unattractive waste product is then
dumped in huge deposits of tailings—ugly mountains
of worthless wastes. That is, worthless, until it was
discovered that these gold-bearing ores contained several times more uranium than they did gold. This had

been known for some time but was rediscovered by Dr. George W. Bain, Canadian-born geologist now a professor at Amherst College. He had picked up some samples of gold ore while surveying South Africa and had put them aside in his laboratory at Amherst. As a consultant to the atomic bomb project, he remembered these dust-gathering specimens and was surprised to discover that Geiger counters showed them to be radioactive. Even so, the ore was not in the same class with Shinkolobwe or Eldorado minerals, and it was not until the demand for uranium became extreme that the U.S. decided to exploit the South African gold ores. On an average a single ton of this gold ore contains about half a pound of uranium or less. This is not very much, but millions of tons of gold tailings are heaped up above ground ready for easy processing.

Late in 1950, the U.S., the United Kingdom and the Union of South Africa signed agreements for the production of uranium with the U.S. getting a minimum of 60 per cent of the output. Sixteen processing plants were built to extract the uranium both from the discarded slimes and from currently produced gold ore. To give some idea of the scale of this project, one plant alone can process a hundred thousand tons of ore per month. When all the plants are running full blast, more than twenty million tons of ore will be processed annually! If we assume that every ten tons of ore yields three pounds of uranium, this means that South African production alone totals six thousand tons of the magic mineral. This product is shipped to the U.S.A. in the form of a heavy yellow sludge called U_3O_8 (uranium oxide), known to miners as U-308, and is packaged in heavy-duty thirty-gallon metal drums.

Just as new discoveries in Africa ranked with the original Shinkolobwe and will probably outdistance it, so, too, do recent discoveries in Canada outclass the original Eldorado. Gilbert LaBine, despite his sixty-one years, again took to the field and explored the rugged wastelands of northern Canada and struck it rich at Lake Athabaska. His Gunnar Mines at Beaver Lodge Lake got a five-year production contract from the Canadian government totaling $160 million. The Saskatchewan deposits were heralded as outranking the original Eldorado finds, but these, too, were soon outclassed by new strikes on the north shore of Lake Huron in the Blind River area.

A Canadian geologist, Franc Joubin, surveyed the Blind River area in 1949 and found radioactivity but no uranium. This was puzzling, and he returned four years later to investigate this peculiarity. He soon found that uranium had been leached out of surface deposits, leaving residual radioactivity. Upon testing the underlying rock with a diamond drill, Joubin hit uranium and soon found that the entire area contained exploitable beds of the much-sought-after mineral. A uranium rush broke out, and soon the Blind River area was overrun with prospectors anxious to stake out their claims. Joubin had hurriedly sought financial aid and had beat the rush of outsiders by staking out over a thousand claims. The Canadian government has contracted with Pronto, Algom and Consolidated Denison companies to the tune of $444 million and has guaranteed a market at premium prices (six dollars per pound of U_3O_8 as a minimum—but the real figure is closer to ten dollars) up to March, 1962. Mill capacity in the Blind River area alone will run around twenty-five thousand tons of ore per day by the end of 1958. It is estimated that the Blind River beds rival those of South Africa and contain over a hundred million tons of ore. No wonder that Canada looks forward to a $180 million business in uranium by 1958.

Elsewhere around the world important finds have been uncovered, with potentially vast deposits being unearthed in Australia. Hunters discovered rich ore beds there as an unexpected payoff of two hunting expeditions. Jack White, an old hand at prospecting, was after other game when he stumbled upon the Rum Jungle deposits. Actually, he was looking for kangaroos when he spotted signs of uranium. The Australian government rewarded White with a tax-free fifty-six-thousand-dollar bonus.

Three other Australian hunters also found their expedition ending up with unexpected game. Stalking bullocks in desolate northern country, they gave chase to an animal which they had wounded and finally cornered and killed the bullock in a remote valley. Mineral formations caught their eye, and they returned with a Geiger counter to discover valuable uranium ore; in fact, so valuable that they disdained the government's bonus and worked the property for themselves.

The Atomic Energy Commission posted its guaranteed prices for domestic uranium ore in 1948, but nothing much came of this incentive until one day in 1952. It was a hot dusty day in Utah, when a young Texas geologist hit pay dirt about forty miles southeast of the town of Moab. AEC experts and other prospectors had explored the surface before thirty-three-year-old Charlie Steen arrived on the scene and they had found no uranium. Steen, who had dabbled in prospecting for oil and tin, reasoned that uranium might be well below the surface and he borrowed money to drill a test hole in the area. The drill which he had borrowed broke off short of his target depth, and Steen, dejected, stuffed some rock cores in his pocket. Stopping at a gas station, he encountered an attendant who was demonstrating radioactivity of some ore samples. Steen, who was too broke to own a Geiger counter, remembered his rock samples and asked the gas attendant to test them. Much to his astonishment the Geiger counter flipped off scale. He wasted no time in staking out his claim and the uranium rush was on in U.S.A.

Steen's strike contains a vast quantity of uranium ore well above the AEC's minimum U_3O_8 requirements which specify that the ore be higher than 0.1 per cent uranium oxide. Much of his ore assayed half a per cent so that Steen was able to exploit his mines profitably. In fact, he took out over a million dollars' worth of ore in less than a year and believes that he has touched only a small fraction of the total reserve.

Other prospectors, like Vernon Pick of Minnesota, opened up new ore beds, and today the region known as the Colorado Plateau, bracketing Arizona, New Mexico, Colorado and Utah, boasts of over one thousand working uranium mines. A steady stream of ore is flowing from mine to mill. And from the mills comes more of the yellow cake which forms the basic feed material of our huge atomic energy plants. America is on its way toward becoming self-sufficient in uranium, but it still shops abroad for as much uranium as it can get. The reason is, of course, to increase the nuclear stockpile and swell the numbers of "nukes" for the bomb stockpile. The military demand for uranium has put such a premium on the metal that it is developing into a half-billion-dollar a year business.

Will we ever get enough uranium? Or bombs? What will happen to the uranium market when guarantees on uranium prices terminate? We cannot answer these questions at the present stage of the game, although it does seem that a point will be reached when even the most conservative general will admit he has enough bombs. For the present and for the near future, the market is based almost entirely upon military needs. Nuclear power is still in its infancy and does not promise to consume appreciable portions of the uranium production until well after 1960.

In discussing uranium and the stockpile, it is well to point out that the usual way of talking about "numbers of bombs in stockpile" is rather meaningless. It is more meaningful to discuss the number of tons of bomb stuff turned out by Oak Ridge and Hanford type plants. This bomb stuff can then be converted into bombs of various powers.

Do we have any way of knowing how much bomb stuff these secret plants turn out each year? In answer to this question, I may cite my own estimates. However, I want to warn that my estimates were soon to be made obsolete by the unexpected development of cheap, easy-to-produce nuclear explosives for large, economy-size bombs. Still, the estimate I made a few years ago is worth explaining for it represents the only true way in which one could measure an atomic arms race.

I was stimulated to make my estimate of the U.S. atomic stockpile by a remark which Senator McMahon made before his untimely death. He had said that he thought it would be possible for the Soviets to estimate our atomic stockpile within an accuracy of 15 per cent. So I set out to see what I could do for myself. I realized at the outset that I did not have the great resources of the Soviet intelligence forces, but I did have a file full of data which might be useful. It was as fascinating as solving a mystery, and although I would never know if my final answer were correct, nevertheless I was hopeful that I might get certain independent checks on my estimate.

Let me remark that I had never been given either production, raw material or stockpile data in any of my official connections with the AEC or MED. And by the summer of 1953, when I made the estimate, I had forgotten relevant pieces of data which might be useful. Bit by bit, I put the pieces of the jigsaw together and I was surprised to see that there were five independent methods for estimating our output of bomb material. I shall not go into the technical details, except to say that they involved data taken from open sources such as Congressional records and hearings. For example, the consumption of electricity at Oak Ridge, the procurement of uranium, the financial data on AEC operations and references given by Defense Department and AEC officials in their speeches.

Based upon these sources, I prepared two graphs. One showed the annual production of bomb stuff from 1945 through 1960. The other represented the total stockpile (in tons of fissionable material) for each year. Frankly, I was astonished when I looked up from my graphs to see just what the figures meant. Thirty tons of bomb stuff per year! I was shocked for this could mean six thousand bombs per year, according to our previous example. My first reaction was to question my calculations. I must be off somewhere, I thought, yet when I examined the data carefully I found that independent methods gave essentially the same answer. I could not do as well as Senator McMahon had said, for I estimated my accuracy as being about 20 per cent although one method might be off as much as 30 per cent. The important thing was that the various estimates checked with one another. . . . I couldn't be far off base.

As I added up the annual production to get the total bomb stockpile, I gasped. The stockpile topped the hundred-ton figure and quickly zoomed to two hundred tons by the year 1958! This was production undreamed of during the war. What sort of military uses could one possibly find for such vast quantities of explosives? All in all it added up to explosives equivalent to ten billion tons of TNT! Or five thousand times more than we dropped on Germany throughout the ceaseless, year-long air raids of World War II. And, as we shall see, this calculus did not reckon with the unexpected breakthrough which made it unnecessary to have Oak Ridge and Hanford type plants to make material for superbombs.

chapter 6

THE NUCLEAR FAMILY OF WEAPONS

Gordon Dean, affable lawyer friend of Senator McMahon, who took over the helm of the AEC from David Lilienthal, spoke of a "family of nuclear weapons" in describing the bomb program of the atomic project. Since he first put this label on the assortment of modern bombs, the family has grown and spawned odd offspring which resemble their parents only in that all retain the "nuke" as their vital heart.

We have just concluded a brief analysis of the spectacular rise in the production of "nuke" material. Now we shall see how this expensive bomb stuff can be molded into a variety of weapons.

The basic purpose for developing a panoply of nuclear gadgets has been to convert the A-bomb into a more flexible weapon, one which could replace the massed fire of ordinary artillery, or substitute for a hail of anti-aircraft shells, or replace an air armada armed with a thousand TNT bombs. In other words, the nuclear family would fulfill Senator McMahon's requirement for "an atomic Army, Navy and Air Force."

Our starting point for the family was a pair of parents—the Thin Man and the Fat Man—oddly enough, both masculine. The Hiroshima weapon or Thin Man was a long cylindrical device, rugged in construction but quite extravagant in its consumption of "nuke" material. The Nagasaki bomb or Fat Man was a big package just fitting into the bomb bay of a B-29 bomber. It was a less rugged device, and its size may be inferred from the fact that for several years the Air Force specified a bomb load capacity of ten thousand pounds for its strategic bombers. The Fat Man packed a punch equal to twenty thousand tons of TNT or twenty kilotons (kt) in the language of the weapons experts. The Thin Man in its original form was a 15-kt gadget.

In talking of the 1945 model A-bombs, I want to emphasize that they were puny and primitive. Hardly engineered to mass production, they were breadboard designs, awkward in appearance and wasteful in their use of bomb material. This is not meant as hindsight criticism of the bombs, for it is the rule in weapon development of any kind that perfection is never reached in the first hatching of a new device. Such proved to be the case with nuclear weapons.

Weapon development suffered a severe hiatus following Nagasaki, due to the uncertain transition from military to civilian control of the Los Alamos laboratory in New Mexico. The first team and much of the second string of nuclear scientists deserted Los Alamos to return to their peacetime pursuits. In addition, the transfer of direction from Groves to Lilienthal more or less isolated the military from the bomb. But perhaps the biggest factor delaying the growth of the nuclear family was the absence of a national policy regarding bomb tests. Los Alamos scientists might dream up designs for new "nukes" and new detonation schemes, but these would remain in the realm of fancy until they could be "proved out" in an actual "bang."

There were only two U.S. bangs of atomic origin from the summer of 1945 through the spring of 1948. These were Bikini Able and Baker shots of 1946. Neither advanced the art of bomb design since they were 1945-style bombs detonated by the military to see what effect they would have upon the Navy's postwar plans. I might add that some Los Alamos experts like Dr. Edward Teller were most unhappy about the Navy's use of 1945-model bombs. I heard that Dr. Teller said that one condition for his staying at Los Alamos would be a greatly accelerated bomb test schedule. Teller had in mind a dozen bomb tests a year!

Those of us who were involved in *Operation Crossroads* at Bikini in the summer of 1946, and who got stuck with the job of analyzing the results, pressed for more bomb tests. However, we were running against the tide and the military did not seem inclined to push for more rapid A-testing. When the Atomic Energy Commission took over the atomic development program, the military seemed resigned to a passive, advisory role in nuclear weaponry. At the time I was working in the Pentagon as a scientific advisor on atomic energy, and I recall having a heated argument with a major general over the War Department's role in atomic energy. I was told that the legal experts (the colonels who attach themselves to generals to prevent them from making mistakes are known as "legal eagles" in the Pentagon) had read the Atomic Energy Act of 1946, and that they had deduced that the War Department was excluded from participating in weapon development. I was floored by the legalistic, matter-of-fact way in which military men conducted their affairs in the clinical atmosphere of the Pentagon. What amazed me was that many of the star-bearers in that five-sided building put their personal security (i.e., promotion) above the interests of national security. I was new to Washington and had yet to learn the truism that an officer insures advancement if he does not make a practice of sticking his neck out.

Pressure built up slowly, but finally in the spring of 1948 the AEC and the Defense Department merged their resources in a Joint Task Force and established the Eniwetok Proving Grounds. Known as *Operation Sandstone*, the first test series included detonation of four experimental "nuclear devices" on separate islands in the Eniwetok Atoll. This formation in the Marshall Islands is an acorn-shaped string of low-lying islands twenty-five by seventeen miles in dimension. The "shot islands" were clustered in the northeast corner of the lagoon and bore the tongue-twisting names—Engebi, Aomon, Biijiri and Runit. The last-named island was most appropriately named.

Many people are perplexed by the term "device" which the AEC uses in describing its weapons tests. Newsmen often interpret this to mean that the gadget tested is not a *bomb* but is rather a prototype or laboratory assembly which could not be used as a droppable weapon. In reality the "device" may be either a laboratory experiment or a workable bomb; it so happens that the use of the term is a technicality which the AEC prefers in order to keep its "cognizance" of the device. Perfected "bombs" come within the province and authority of the military.

The devices tested at Eniwetok in the spring of 1948 consisted of four designs, all pretty much along the lines of the Fat Man. The AEC's principal design criterion was a bigger and more efficient "bang." In other words, more kilotons per "nuke" and more bang per pound of "nuke" material. Thus, the emphasis in these four *Sandstone* shots was mainly nuclear as opposed to engineering of the bomb package.

Senator Edwin C. Johnson, later Governor of Colorado, gave us some idea of how big a bang the AEC experts achieved when he revealed: "Now our scientists already have created a bomb that has six times the effectiveness of the bomb that was dropped at Nagasaki." Which, in the arithmetic of the bomb experts, meant 120 kilotons. No indication has been given as to how much more economical the "nukes" were in releasing their pent-up kilotons, but it seems reasonable to assume that these tests paved the way for doubling the efficiency of nuclear explosives. To put it another way, the new designs really led to a doubling of the stockpile since each pound of bomb stuff could be used twice as effectively.

Some clue as to the ease with which bigger bangs might be obtained is to be gleaned from testimony which bomb expert Edward Teller gave before Senator McMahon's group early in 1946. "The atomic bomb is in its infancy," asserted the Budapest-born physicist, "and even a moderate amount of work may improve it considerably. Future bombs may become less expensive, may be easier to handle, and they may have a much greater destructive power." Significantly, he added: "I am convinced that it will not be very difficult to construct atomic bombs which will dwarf the Hiroshima bomb in the same way that that bomb has dwarfed high explosives." These were to be prophetic words, yet the *Sandstone* tests were only a beginning, and hardly even "modest" in the sense that Dr. Teller had in mind.

All four shots at Eniwetok consisted of detonations from high iron towers. Although two of the islands were scarcely more than sandspits, reinforced with concrete foundations, they did not disappear under the sea. In fact, survey parties were able to re-enter the tower area shortly after each burst. The radioactive fall-out which characterized later bomb tests was not serious in the *Sandstone* series. The important aspect of the 1948 tests was that they provided experimental evidence for certain theories of weapon design and thus provided Los Alamos experts with valuable data which could be used in developing more potent "nukes." The stage was set for the appearance of bigger bombs.

However, there was a three-year delay before more bombs were fired at Eniwetok. It was not until April of 1951 that Los Alamos experts were able to test new bomb designs. Thus, from Nagasaki until *Operation Greenhouse* in the spring of 1951 the U.S.A. had only one test series—a period of almost six years. It took the jolt of Korea to accelerate our nuclear test program. Korea served to focus attention not so much on high-yield or big weapons as it did to underline the need for smaller or low-yield weapons. Such weapons would, it was felt, be more useful on the battlefield where they would substitute for massed artillery fire.

The development of the small A-bomb or tactical weapon has had a devious history. In January of 1951 the Atomic Energy Commission established its Nevada Proving Grounds for proof-testing of small bombs. Yet three years before I recall a meeting of scientist advisors and military men in which the issue of small bombs came to a head. The meeting took place in the conference room on the second floor of the AEC's headquarters on Constitution Avenue across from the main Navy Building. At this conference General Lewis H. Brereton headed up the military membership of the committee while James Conant, Robert Oppenheimer and Crawford Greenewalt, now president of du Pont, rounded out the civilian group. Dr. Conant presided over the meeting and proceeded to run down items on the agenda in a brisk fashion. I had visited Conant the week before to warn him about some Air Force politicking on the last agenda item, and he had looked across his sparsely furnished Harvard office and frowned as though in disbelief. I had learned in the Pentagon that the Air Force would veto the last agenda item and had lined up Army support to defeat the Navy in its drive to have the AEC develop a smaller and lighter bomb. Up to that time the Air Force had a monopoly on delivery of the A-bomb, and it did not relish the idea of the bomb being made small enough for naval aircraft to carry it.

Sure enough, when Conant came to the last item of business, he found that the new weapon development was vetoed. Declaring the meeting over, Conant leaned back and looked at General Brereton and at Admiral "Deac" Parsons, the Navy's top bomb expert.

I was sitting directly across from Parsons and saw him give Conant a tight grin and throw up his hands. Brereton looked sheepish and apologetically said, "I had no choice. I had an instructed vote." I think that this was Conant's first bitter taste of interservice feuding, and he was disgusted by it. Naturally, it set back the whole development of small, lightweight weapons.

These new bombs were first given field trials in prototype form early in 1951, when the AEC opened up its Nevada Proving Grounds northwest of Las Vegas and northeast of Death Valley. There at Yucca Flats, in flat country inhabited only by range cattle and a few Gila monsters, the AEC tested an even dozen "nuke" designs in 1951 and almost the same number in succeeding years. All the shots were small bombs, usually less than thirty kilotons in blast power. The reason why so many tests were necessary is that the bomb designers were up against two conflicting requirements. First, the bomb package had to be made as rugged and as small as possible. Second, the "nuke" had to be as efficient as possible in order not to waste ten-thousand-dollar-per-pound bomb stuff. Unfortunately, as the bomb package was shrunk in size the "nuke" efficiency dropped off. Moreover, there was a lower limit to how little bomb stuff you could get to chain react because of the element of critical size.

For example, if you wanted to test out a new design of a weapon for use as a missile warhead, you could not just set off one detonation and get all the data you needed. You would have to fire several shots in order to get "points on a curve" so that you would know the optimum design of the weapon. Combine this feature with the variety of different classes of weapons requested by the military and it is obvious why many bomb tests were required. These Nevada tests provided the experimental basis for developing nuclear warheads for a variety of missiles, torpedoes (naval and aerial), artillery shells, aircraft interception, mines and, of course, aerial bombs. Thus, the junior members of the nuclear family were many and diverse. Because of their relatively poor efficiency, and mostly because of the many numbers demanded by the military, these tactical or small weapons imposed a severe demand upon the atomic stockpile. In fact, as we shall see, it is the requirement for these weapons that keeps the AEC production plants in full operation today.

Let us now return to the Eniwetok Proving Grounds where the big members of the nuclear family receive their baptism. We have mentioned that the 1948 test series developed a 120-kt explosive. The 1951 series boosted this bang fourfold. President Eisenhower revealed in 1953 that we developed an A-bomb "twenty-five times as powerful as the weapons with which the atomic age dawned. . . ." Such a weapon would correspond to about one half million tons of TNT. It represents a practical limit (in the light of present knowledge, it is beyond the economic limit) for bombs which derive their energy solely from a chain reaction in expensive "nuke" material. While it would be possible to construct still larger A-bombs, this would be self-defeating since the difficulty of assembling so many critical masses in such a weapon and the exorbitant cost of the active material makes the A-bomb a poor choice for still larger bombs. Yet the tests at *Operation Greenhouse* in 1951 did throw light on how still bigger bombs might be made.

The quest for a bomb more powerful than one million tons of TNT (or a megaton weapon), oddly enough, began before the original A-bomb was developed. When I visited Los Alamos during the war I poked my head in one unoccupied room and saw a maze of copper tubes, valves and gadgets. "What in the world is that?" I asked a friend. He replied cryptically, "That's Super."

Super was the name for the hydrogen bomb which Los Alamos experts abandoned in order to intensify work on an A-bomb. Super would have to wait until after the war when more data became available. It was simply too tough a job to tackle during the war. So Super was put on the shelf, and only occasionally did some weapons experts do any work on it. After the 1946 Bikini bomb tests, scientists at Los Alamos dreamed up a "thermonuclear system," for which read "hydrogen bomb," but they came to a dead end when it turned out that they could not finish their calculations. High-speed electronic computing machines were needed, and at the time none were in existence which could do the job.

The turning point in Super's history came in the fall of 1949 when scientists were shocked by the news of the Soviet nuclear test which signaled the end to our atomic monopoly. Scientists inside and outside Los Alamos worried over the significance of the Soviet bomb. One scientist, Dr. Luis Alvarez, handsome, blond physicist who had flown in the observation plane at Hiroshima, kept a diary of his worries so that I can document some of the events which brought Super to the AEC conference table for decision. In September of 1949 the brilliant young Alvarez became excited over the Soviet success in their atomic program and went to Professor E. O. Lawrence and Edward Teller to see if the United States might somehow or other recoup after its loss of A-bomb monopoly. The trio agreed that Super was the answer and they set out to get things rolling. They were driven by a fear that the Soviets were already on the trail of Super and, as Alvarez expressed it: ". . . If they did make it, that would give them a great jump ahead of us and essentially nullify our stockpile of atomic weapons." Lawrence, Alvarez and Teller embarked upon a ricochet plane trip across the country, stopping off at Los Alamos and Washington, D.C., to agitate for a crash program on Super. One of their first thoughts was to build immediately new reactors which would produce extra-heavy hydrogen (technically known as tritium), which seemed all-important to the success of an H-bomb.

Inside Los Alamos, the laboratory director, Dr. Norris Bradbury, who had taken over when Oppenheimer left the laboratory, was also worried about the Soviet bomb. He, too, was thinking about Super and whether it might not be the best answer to the Soviet A-bomb. As Bradbury put it: "The fall of 1949 was really a crossroads in the atomic energy business." The Los Alamos laboratory had to decide whether it would go on the same road in designing bigger A-bombs or go off into the unknown and risk a dubious venture in the area of thermonuclear weapons.

An argument over the H-bomb seethed behind the white façade of the Atomic Energy Commission's Constitution Avenue headquarters and it centered upon Dr. J. Robert Oppenheimer, the chairman of the AEC's General Advisory Committee. It was a within-the-family argument, but an alert Washington *Post* editor, Alfred Friendly, got wind of it and put a whole bunch of tidbits of information together which added up to "H-bomb controversy" and, of course, a terrific headline for the Washington *Post*. Rather than break his story without consulting the AEC, Al Friendly went to David Lilienthal and laid his cards on the table. The AEC chairman turned chalk-white and pleaded, "Al, I have never asked a newsman to kill a story, but please hold off until the President has a chance to decide this issue." Al Friendly killed his story.

Again, it was Colorado's "Big Ed" Johnson who broke the story on a nationwide television program. The date was November 1, 1949, and the place was a TV studio in New York City. Big Ed had hurried up from Washington to go on the air. Out of the blue, the Senator (a member of the elite Joint Committee on Atomic Energy) blurted out, "Here's the thing that is top secret. Our scientists from the time the bombs were detonated at Hiroshima and Nagasaki have been trying to make what is known as a super-bomb. They want one that has a thousand times the effect of that terrible bomb—and that's the secret, the big secret that scientists in America are so anxious to divulge to the whole scientific world."

The scientists may have been anxious to discuss the great issues involved in the decision to make the superbomb but they never took security into their own hands as Senator Johnson did. In fact, the record of the scientists in this respect is practically perfect so far as I know. When secrets have been let out of the bag, the men untying the strings have been senators, generals and government officials. One wonders if the scientists have not been too well behaved.

Senator Johnson maintained stoutly that he had not spilled the beans. He pointed to a statement which John J. McCloy had made in 1946 when he was associated with the War Department. I dug up the reference and found it contained in a speech which the outspoken McCloy, now of the Chase National Bank, had given as Assistant Secretary of War to the National Association of Life Underwriters. "We talk today of the bomb in terms of the equivalent of 20,000 tons of TNT," said McCloy in December of 1946. "From first-hand information given me by the scientists whose prophecies were uncannily accurate during the course of the war, there can be little doubt that within the next 10 years, to be conservative, bombs of the power of 100,000 tons to 250,000 tons of TNT can be made, something over ten times more powerful than the bomb dropped on Hiroshima. And if we can move to the other end of the periodic table and use hydrogen in the generation of energy, we would have a bomb somewhere around 1,000 times as powerful as the Nagasaki bomb."

It should be clear that Mr. McCloy was talking of a "possibility" and not revealing the existence of an

actual secret project or an immediate objective. Nonetheless, McCloy knew what he was talking about, for
as it turned out he *was* on the conservative side.

President Truman's hand was forced by the unexpected pressure which developed following the sena-
torial indiscretion. Late in January of 1950, he made
up his mind with characteristic independence. Personally, I felt at the time, and still feel, that Mr. Truman
had no other wise political choice but to order full
speed ahead on the H-development. This he did on
January 31, 1950, and the race was on to develop
the superbomb, or as Truman called it "the so-called
hydrogen bomb." The words "so-called" were well
advised, although at the time not even Dr. Teller
would have known why.

Scientists interpreted President Truman's go-ahead
on the H-bomb as the green light for public discussion
of the great issues involved. Since Hiroshima many
thoughtful scientists had pondered the morality of
the decision to use the bomb. Arthur Compton spoke
out; so did Harold Urey; and a whole group of former
Los Alamos experts signed a statement urging that
the United States pledge itself never to use the hydrogen bomb first. They concluded: "There can be only
one justification for our development of the hydrogen
bomb, and that is to prevent its use."

The eloquent Dr. Oppenheimer, heading up the
Institute for Advanced Studies at Princeton, spoke out
in an impassioned appeal:

The decision to seek or not to seek international control
of the A-bomb, the decision to try to make or not to make
the H-bomb, are issues, rooted in complex technical mat-

ters, that nevertheless touch the very basis of our morality. There is a grave danger for us in that these decisions have been taken on the basis of facts held secret. This is not because the men who must contribute to the decisions, or must make them, are lacking in wisdom; it is because wisdom itself cannot flourish, nor even truth be determined, without the give and take of debate or criticism. The relevant facts could be of little help to an enemy; yet they are indispensable for an understanding of questions of policy. If we are wholly guided by fear, we shall fail in this time of crisis. The answer to fear cannot always lie in the dissipation of the causes of fear; sometimes it lies in courage.

On the other side of the fence, the dynamic Dr. Teller, who can move exceedingly fast despite an injured leg, challenged his former colleague at Los Alamos. Writing in the *Bulletin of Atomic Scientists,* Teller issued a call to arms, pleading with his fellow physicists to pitch in and help perfect Super. He scolded his scientist friends for their preoccupation with non-scientific aspects of weapons, stating flatly: "It is *not* the scientist's job to determine whether a hydrogen bomb should be constructed, whether it should be used, or how it should be used."

The scientists were worried and they continued to speak out. Their outspokenness perturbed AEC officials, but the real fireworks came when Hans Bethe, Cornell theoretician and father of many thermonuclear ideas, published an article in the *Scientific American.* Or, we should say, tried to publish an article. Dr. Bethe had obligingly sent a copy of his manuscript to the Commission, where it gathered dust while the presses were rolling on his article. Three thousand

copies of the magazine had already been printed when
the AEC stepped in and stopped the presses. Simultaneously, AEC headquarters dispatched telegrams to
its scientists and former employees, telling them in
effect, "Shut your trap." This blunt attempt at muzzling
public discussion angered the scientists, so that three
days later the AEC sent out another bale of messages,
now known as the "Shut your trap, *please*" telegrams.
Dr. Bethe and the editors of the *Scientific American*
extricated themselves from hot water by making a
few trifling changes in the article and the presses
rolled again. But three thousand copies of the magazine were burned and every editor in the country
was singed.

Work on Super went ahead, but the year 1950
ended with many of the top planners dubious about its
chances for success. There were two principal obstacles
which appeared almost insurmountable to some of
the experts. First, everyone agreed that you had to
have an atomic bomb primer or trigger to produce
the extreme temperatures needed to initiate a thermonuclear reaction and to duplicate for a fleeting moment
the conditions inside a star. Late in 1950 it seemed that
the temperature attainable in an A-bomb core would
not be high enough to burn hydrogen material. Second,
everyone agreed that you would need lots of special
hydrogen (tritium), which was difficult to manufacture
and which was so expensive as to make the final
H-bomb an outlandishly costly item. This pessimism
was shared by many and is summed up by Dr. Bradbury's assessment: "The state of knowledge of thermonuclear systems . . . up until the spring of 1951, was

such as to make the practical utility or even the work-ability in any useful sense of what was then imagined as a thermonuclear weapon extremely questionable."

Yet experts, like Teller, were optimistic although they could not put their finger on the reason. The barriers blocking the road to the H-bomb started to disintegrate in the spring of 1951. Two events combined to indicate a new approach toward making the weapon.

Operation Greenhouse, the 1951 test series at Eniwetok Atoll, provided the basic clue. One bomb test was partially designed to determine how well hydrogen fuel might burn in a gigantic A-bomb. The bomb was specially rigged to create the highest temperature ever produced on earth—roughly a hundred million degrees centigrade. Inside the core of the "nuke" there was placed a small quantity of hydrogen fuel. The bomb test proved that hydrogen could be fused, although only in test-tube amounts. One big obstacle now seemed surmountable, namely, the temperature barrier.

This left, however, the very real difficulty of providing the exceedingly expensive special hydrogen. This stuff had to be produced by using the big production plants on the banks of the Columbia River—the very same ones which produce plutonium. By substituting the light element lithium for uranium, a nuclear reaction was produced which gave birth to the special hydrogen. But the cost was fabulous—many times the cost of plutonium. The big break came following the Eniwetok H-experiment when theoretical physicists put their heads together at Los Alamos and concocted a method for minimizing the amount of special hydrogen needed in the bomb. In fact, they came up with an idea which was to change the whole nature of the hydrogen bomb so drastically that the finally perfected weapon must be regarded as a "so-called" H-bomb. The explanation of this unclear sentence will be found in the next chapter.

By the fall of 1952 the experts were ready to make a full field trial of their ideas. They had subjected their theories to the impartial examination of lightning-like electronic computers, then newly developed, and the results seemed assuring. However, the proof of the pudding would have to await an actual test. *Operation Ivy* took place at Eniwetok and the "Mike" shot was designated for November 1, 1952. The shot island was Elugelab, a tiny coral strip which projected only a few feet above the level of the Pacific. When the shot occurred before dawn of Test Day the island was enveloped in an awesome fireball and the whole island disappeared from view. In its place the lagoon waters conceal a yawning mile-wide, 175-foot-deep cavity.

No official announcement has been made about the power of this first so-called H-bomb, but it is reliably estimated that it produced a blast equal to that from eight million tons of TNT—i.e., eight megatons. The world might not have even heard about this test had not some sailors written letters home. Within a week after the "Mike" shot, relatives in the U.S.A. received sensational letters describing the enormous explosion which the sailors had witnessed from thirty miles away. Someone in authority in Joint Task Force 132 had "goofed" and the mail back home had gone uncensored, so the news was out.

On April 7, 1954, the government finally made it official by releasing motion-picture films of the "Mike" shot showing the spectacular explosion. The fireball from this megaton weapon oozed out from Shot Island (Elugelab) until it seemed to almost touch Bogon Island, two miles away. Then the seething mass of fire and flame rushed upward to a height of twenty-five miles, producing the now familiar mushroom cloud. A flicker of heat was felt by the closest observers aboard ship thirty miles away, but no one was hurt by the flash.

The great crushing blast of the explosion rocked the test island, devastating it, as we have seen, and then sent its hammer blow across Bogon Island and smashed on to Engebi, leveling all structures there. Its pile-driving force spent itself as it thundered across the lagoon, producing a sharp shock pattern in the clear, bluish-green water. By the time the shock wave rocketed to Parry Island, twenty miles to the southeast, where the remote control detonation center for other shots is located, it did only minor damage.

The so-called H-bomb was a reality. However, it was by no means a military weapon. In this case, the monstrous device tested on Elugelab Island was not a military deliverable or droppable bomb. Further engineering and more development would be required to convert the experimental gadget into a practical weapon of war. Such a weapon was first tested on March 1, 1954.

chapter 7

THE ACCIDENT—RADIOACTIVE FALL-OUT

Before dawn on the morning of March 1, 1954, there was an accident in the South Pacific. In fact, a series of accidents. It all began when the United States set off its most powerful superbomb.

The bomb was mounted high atop a metal test tower looming over a tiny island site—one of the barren sand corral outcroppings of the Bikini Atoll in the Marshall Islands. To safeguard against accidents a large area of the Pacific Ocean had been staked out and warnings issued to all nations to stay out of range.

When the bomb went off there were twenty-three uninvited and unsuspected observers. They comprised the crew of the tiny Japanese tuna trawler, the *Lucky Dragon.* Those on deck were startled by the spectacle of a "sun" rising precipitously and prematurely in the west. Minutes later when the awesome, orange-red brilliance of the fireball had flared out, the ship felt the acoustic boom of the explosion over a hundred miles away. However, the great distance saved the ship and its crew from any direct harm either from the prodigious heat or the Promethean blast punch of the bomb. Actually, the Japanese were not inside forbidden waters as we defined them. But our search craft had not spotted the tiny ship in the vastness of the Pacific.

Three hours after the bomb detonation, when the real sun was up, the Japanese fishermen got a second shock. This time it did damage. Out of the usually dustless Pacific sky there settled down upon the decks of the not-so-fortunate *Dragon* a swirling precipitation. Tiny but easily visible flecks of greyish white dust fell from the sky and soon dusted the ship and its crew with a talc-like mantle. No one aboard knew anything about radioactivity. Even if they had, one wonders what they would have done. This fall-out of chalky dust was radioactive. It had come over a hundred miles, borne aloft in the grotesque mushroom cloud. Settling out, the fall-out dust alarmed the simple fisherman for it strongly irritated parts of the body, such as the eyes, lips and nasal pasages, where it made contact.

The decision was made to pull in the nets and head for home. It had been a disappointing haul even though they had ventured far to the south to catch the migratory tuna. Two weeks later, the trawler chugged into the home port of Yaizu. At no time had radio silence been broken so that the outside world was unaware of the accident. Had U.S. officials received word, they could have promptly dispatched part of the bomb test task force to the ship and removed the crew. The crew could then have been "decontaminated" by washing and scrubbing; this would certainly have minimized the aftereffects of the fall-out.

As the world now knows, the story hit page one of many newspapers when it was discovered that the fishermen had been burned by the radioactive fall-out. In the home islands the Japanese people were deeply shocked by the sight of the injured fishermen (photographs were featured in many Japanese newspapers).

All the horror of Hiroshima was conjured up by the mere mention of the word radioactivity. In a very real sense the Japanese people were preconditioned to hysteria.

Health authorities in Osaka about 150 miles from Yaizu were jolted into activity by the news accounts of the *Lucky Dragon* which appeared in the morning paper *Yomiuri*. They summoned technical aid from Osaka City University to see if any fish from the hold of the *Fukuryu Maru No. 5* (the *Lucky Dragon*) had reached the Osaka fish market. Scientists soon found that some tuna fish in the market caused their Geiger counters to chatter at a frenzied rate. They discovered that the tuna were contaminated with radioactivity. The news spread rapidly, and overnight the bottom came out of the fish market. Prices plunged but fish consumption dove even more precipitously. Americans might not regard this disturbance in the fish supply as important since it is not the mainstay of our diet. However, fish is to the Japanese what beef is to Americans. It is their major source of protein.

Had only the tuna aboard the *Lucky Dragon* been the culprits, the problem would not have been more than a front-page scare story. But soon other boats fishing in southern waters put in to port with radioactive catches. We shall return to this matter after we reconstruct what happened at Bikini that morning of March 1, 1954.

Let's go back to the scene of the "crime" and see what clues we may piece together to explain the incredible radioactive power of the weapon we tested. The time: 3:50 in the morning well before dawn.

The place: a tiny, low-lying island in the group which forms a scimitar-shaped atoll. The occasion: the experimental detonation of a new nuclear device expected to yield a bang equal to that of about eight million tons of TNT—an engineered version of the "Mike" device tested on November 1, 1952.

Of course, the island was deserted except for unconcerned island rats which scurried over the coral sand, seeking out morsels of food left behind by those man creatures who had so suddenly departed. High atop the metal test tower, which spraddled a concrete base, the "gadget" rested. Elaborate electronic devices, whirring relays and complex timing instruments were going full speed—all set in motion and operated by remote control. Zero hour was approaching . . . the minutes ticked off . . . then, the seconds. Then the actuators slammed home and the massive assembly of TNT explosives detonated, imploding with a million instantaneous hammer blows toward the very center of the "gadget." Nestled inside, the "nuke" or nuclear core of the real bomb stuff collapsed into what physicists call "a supercritical assembly." Meaning that the chain reaction let go!

It worked! What had been cool metal was converted into a raging hot gas in one-millionth of a second. Heavy elements fissioned . . . light elements fused . . . as Professor Einstein's formula of 1905 vintage was tested with a vengeance.

Within seconds a huge, glowing-hot fireball roared into space above the tiny island, flowing out over open ocean with its inferno of heat. It was as though one had dumped down from above the contents of a

million Bessemer furnaces. Man had duplicated the
fiery conditions inside the hottest stars. The blazing
brilliance of the fireball flooded the entire area with
whitish light brighter than that from the noonday sun.
This is what startled the Japanese fishermen about
a hundred miles away.

U.S. observers thirty miles away wore special glasses
to view the spectacle after the initial flash started to
wane. Even through these dense filters the orange-red
fireball was awesome in appearance. It spread out into
a bulging sphere, flattened at the bottom where it
squatted on the earth, reaching a diameter of three and
a half miles.

Underneath the incandescent ball of fire the island
felt the savage fury of the concussion. Millions of tons
of the substratum were dislodged by the pummeling.
All of the bomb parts and accessories were instantane-
ously volatilized as was the majority of the test tower.
Thousands of tons of concrete vanished into wisps of
powder. Coral was vaporized and swept into the churning fireball. Task Force observers were transfixed as
the fireball started heavenward, changing as it rose
into an extravaganza of colored fire masses. Below, the
island, or rather what had been an island, was cloaked
in a deep violet haze—an eerie glow produced by the
intense radioactivity ionizing atoms of air.

Slowly at first and then ever faster the remnants of
the explosion shot upward to form the all too familiar
mushroom cloud. The top of the bomb cloud pierced
the stratosphere. Measurements showed that parts of
it went over a hundred thousand feet above the earth.
Then the persistent sideward push of the upper air

tilted the mushroom stem and pushed the grotesque formation downwind.

Some of the shattered island debris fell back to earth almost at once, plunging into the cavity scooped out of the earth's crust. Some of the tiny particles sucked up into the cloud went all the way up to the stratosphere and then proceeded to circle the globe. These globe-straddling bomb particles are not visible to the naked eye but readily tell their tale to Geiger counters. In fact, these tattletale atoms constitute the means by which each nation "snoops" on the bomb-testing operations of the other. Measurements have become so refined that the British were able to identify atoms from the March 1st explosion a year afterward.

Up to March 1, 1954, the bomb experts knew that you had to expect radioactive material near the test site and also all around the globe. The thing they didn't worry enough about was what might happen, say, a hundred or two hundred miles away. True, they waited for "favorable meteorology" so that inhabited islands in the Marshalls would not be in the probable path of the bomb cloud. But on March 1, 1954, something went wrong. The winds shifted and the bomb cloud went sailing where it wasn't supposed to go. It drifted over the *Lucky Dragon,* and some three hours after the blast the Japanese fishermen were amazed to see dust falling on their tiny boat.

Shi no hai they later called the whitish gray flecks which continued to swirl down on them, meaning literally "ashes of death." But at the time they knew nothing of the lethal character of the fall-out. However, they promptly set out for home, as we have already related. That night, according to Japanese reports, some of the crew fell ill. They became nauseated and suffered a loss of appetite akin to seasickness; but the sea was calm that night and the fishermen were all used to the ups and downs of seafaring, so they could not have been seasick. Moreover, parts of their skin where the chalklike dust had settled became inflamed, tender to touch and later painful.

Remember that these men aboard the *Fukuryu Maru* were simple fishing folk, unversed in such things as radioactivity. They simply did not know enough to decontaminate themselves or the ship. Thus, the ship stayed radioactive and penetrating rays from the dust bombarded the crew night and day all the way back to port. It was as though there was a gigantic X-ray machine in the hold and you couldn't turn it off.

Once in port the men were treated for radiation sickness as doctors quickly diagnosed the illness. Three days after the boat put into Yaizu, Professor N. Masanori came down from Tokyo University and measured the radioactivity still on board. The little boat was still "hot" and caused the professor's radiation meter to buzz quite ominously. His meter registered up to a hundred milliroentgens per hour or almost fifty times the peacetime allowable rate set by experts—and this was more than two weeks after the explosion.

At the same time some of the gray-white dust in the cracks of the wooden deck was gathered up for analysis. A team of skilled research workers at Kyoto University went to work on this pinch of dust. For the moment we shall leave them hard at work and return to them later.

Medical reports on the condition of the Japanese fishermen indicate that they must have received a total dose of about two hundred roentgens of radiation. This roughly one-half of the lethal dose. One of the crew, radioman Aikichi Kuboyama, later died on September 23, 1954, apparently from secondary effects. All the others recovered from their illness, and I believe that most of them are back at sea.

When I first heard about the accident in the Pacific I was deeply puzzled. Why, I asked myself, should an H-bomb injure anyone a hundred miles away? An H-bomb, I reasoned, should not be very radioactive. How then was it possible for there to be so much radioactivity so far from the testing point?

I recalled that when we tested the world's first A-bomb at Alamogordo, New Mexico, we had a curious aftereffect. The bomb was detonated on a high tower in the dreary wasteland well away from any city. Unknown to us, there were some cattle grazing peacefully about ten or fifteen miles from the tower. Later, when they were rounded up, it was noticed that the hide and hair on their backs was spotted with white where some of the bomb residue had fallen from the sky. Thus, the first time we tested an A-bomb we had a taste of fall-out—a kind of mild forecast of things to come.

Still, the radioactive fall-out at Alamogordo was weak stuff compared with what the Japanese fishermen must have received in order to produce the observed symptoms of radiation sickness. Then, I remembered my experiences at Bikini in the summer of 1946. We called it Bikini Baker—the second shot in

Operation Crossroads. A Nagasaki-type bomb was suspended about halfway to the bottom of the ocean floor in the center of a target fleet of ships. Surely, almost everyone is familiar with the famous photographs of this underwater shot showing the cauliflower excrescence of the bomb cloud. The ships were drenched in a radioactive rain-out of lethal power.

Reflecting over the phenomena of Alamogordo and Bikini Baker in 1945 and 1946, I tried to connect these two seemingly unrelated tests. I had to puzzle out how one could have a fall-out of Bikini Baker lethality over one hundred miles downwind. To be sure, the power of the 1954 bomb was immense, being revealed by Congressional sources as between fourteen and sixteen megatons; about twice what the experts had expected. But that was blast power, and since the bomb was supposed to be an H-bomb it should not be very radioactive. It was a thousand times the blast power of the Hiroshima bomb, but its radioactive potency should not be a thousand times more.

The radioactivity of the H-bomb should be greater than that of the Hiroshima bomb or the Bikini Baker shot, but only to the extent that the A-bomb trigger in the superbomb produced split atoms of uranium. Reasoning that it would take a jumbo-sized trigger to set off the H-bomb, I made some estimates with a slide rule. My slide rule turned out a distressing answer. The radioactivity was ten times too small to produce the "right answer," meaning the fall-out I knew must have occurred on the *Lucky Dragon.* The only way I could jigger up the calculation was to assume a localized fall-out on the *Lucky Dragon.* Not

only would this be highly unlikely but I had a few fragments of data about a serious fall-out on Rongelap
Island 110 miles from Bikini and considerably south
of the *Lucky Dragon.*

Now there was a possibility that the H-bomb might
induce radioactivity in the island itself. So I set about
calculating this effect. Two weeks later, groggy from
tedious computation, I concluded this could not be the
answer.

I was frustrated. In fact, I felt like a student who
knows the right answer to a problem but can't work it
out. Then, I remembered how I had often been forced
to work problems backward, using the answer given
in a textbook. So I set about going backward from the
Lucky Dragon to Bikini rather than vice versa. The
analytic roadwork is too complex to explain in non-
mathematical language, but in ordinary terms I deduced what must have been detonated in the bomb
in order to dose the fishermen with radioactive fall-
out. My calculations convinced me that the substance
which hurt the fishermen was the same as that from an
ordinary A-bomb. Specifically, split atoms of uranium!

In fact, the mathematics of the deductive process
permitted no other interpretation. There was no other
means to account for the unique radioactivity measured
by Japanese scientists.

Having "solved" the problem, I was in a quandary.
Here is why I was again perplexed. My calculations
indicated that somewhat less than a ton of uranium
bomb stuff would have to be fissioned in the bomb to
produce the observed fall-out. Remember how we have
already described the bomb stuff. It's difficult to pro-

duce uranium-235 (or plutonium), costing about ten thousand dollars per pound. This would mean an investment in "our Bikini bomb" of about twenty million dollars. But this is not the main objection. As we have shown by our description of bomb assembly, the critical size of the bomb stuff would make such an enormous conglomeration impossible to assemble in a practical weapon.

There was an obvious way out of the dilemma. Namely, to assume that the bomb-makers had succeeded in fissioning *ordinary* uranium. In other words, U^{238} which constitutes 99.3 per cent of natural uranium. Ordinary uranium could not be used in an ordinary A-bomb because it would not sustain a chain reaction. That's why we built the huge separation plants at Oak Ridge, and later at Paducah, Kentucky, and Portsmouth, Ohio—to strip away the valuable U^{235} from the worthless U^{238}. The former would work in a chain reaction; the latter would not.

After beating my head against the hard walls of this dilemma, I found a small crack which invited exploration. Was it possible, I asked myself, that the H-bomb was a steppingstone to the utilization of cheap uranium? I knew that natural uranium could be fissioned, not with neutrons from a chain reaction, but with neutrons heated up to high speed. Perhaps, the superbomb did this very trick!

I shall not take the uninitiate through the labyrinth of nuclear physics involved in exploring this possibility. It's sufficient to say that the idea looked good. Rather crude calculations made it look even better. Furthermore, a lot of previously disconnected tidbits of information suddenly made sense.

It all added up to the following explanation of what happened inside the superbomb that morning in March, 1954.

First, an A-bomb trigger detonated. This probably had a force greater than the punch of a hundred thousand tons of TNT. It was really a double trigger, releasing tremendous heat and at the same time uncorking a burst of fission neutrons.

Second, an H-phase flared up in the bomb under the combined blowtorch effect of the trigger and the action of the neutrons. The latter struck a liner of lithium (probably lithium deuteride, an opalescent white compound of lithium and heavy hydrogen). When neutrons hit lithium they initiate a well-known nuclear reaction that liberates helium and tritium. We know that tritium is the rarest breed of hydrogen and is most inflammable as a nuclear fuel when combined with deuterium. And there they were, both the necessary ingredients, one waiting and the other produced on the spot. The trigger's heat plus the running jump provided by the tritium's birth caused the two forms of hydrogen to fuse together. So the H-bomb was partly an H-bomb after all! But it was more. The thermonuclear reaction which fused the hydrogen into helium did something else. It released a vast flood of very fast neutrons—much speedier than those liberated in the fission process.

Third, these speedy neutrons shot out into the outer mantle of the bomb. And what was this outer jacket? It should be rather obvious by now that it was an overcoat of ordinary, cheap uranium. The fast nuclear projectiles liberated in fusion fissioned this jacket, not in a chain reaction but rather in an awesome broadside bombardment. This made ordinary uranium just as blast-producing as the expensive bomb stuff made at Oak Ridge. One ton of this cheap uranium, costing about thirty-five thousand dollars, has a total power equal to the blast from eighteen million tons of TNT.

At Bikini man was able to smash through the barrier which had kept cheap uranium in the untouchable category. In so doing he thrust the world into a completely different kind of arms race, which we shall discuss later. Of course, he also perfected a weapon with immense radioactive killing power.

I was pretty sure of myself by now, but after all I was depending on armchair calculations. I had no access to the highly secret test data which could confirm my theorizing. But I did have access to some Japanese data.

Let's go back to the laboratory where Japanese chemists busied themselves working over a pinch of talc-like dust scraped from the deck of the *Lucky Dragon*. Weeks dragged by as the patient scientists separated out one element after another from the mixture in the sample. They quickly confirmed that radioactive elements in their test tubes corresponded to those released in the fission of uranium. This was comforting to me and backed up my calculations.

I received a copy of the scientific articles prepared by the Japanese scientists so I was kept informed of their work. Some of these papers appeared in a special 133-page issue of the *Bulletin of the Institute for Chemical Research* (Kyoto University), but long before I saw this treatise on fall-out dust, I managed to get a copy of an article appearing in the August, 1954, issue of *Bunseki Kagaku*. The latter is the *Japan Analyst*, a highly scholarly publication distributed internationally. In an article titled "Analysis of Bikini Ash," Professor K. Kimura of the University of Tokyo summarized some of the results which Japanese scientists had obtained by the end of May following the Bikini blast. I knew of Dr. Kimura from research work which he had done before the war. In a 1940 issue of the U.S. *Physical Review* he and his colleagues had reported on the discovery of a new form of uranium produced in a cyclotron experiment. This new variant was U^{237}, a highly radioactive substance with a half-life of one week.

Fate had quite a surprise in store for Dr. Kimura. Uranium-237 was found in the dirty dust from the *Lucky Dragon's* deck. His oriental calm must have been shattered for he wrote: "It was truly a source of profound emotion when, during the present experiments . . . U^{237} was unexpectedly again encountered."

If Dr. Kimura was profoundly impressed, I was flabbergasted. Not that Kimura had found something in 1954 on the deck of a tuna trawler, something which he had produced fifteen years before with a cyclotron, but that this immediately confirmed my theory. This may not be apparent to a layman, but to any nuclear scientist it was obvious. You see, U^{237} is produced in a cyclotron by bombarding lithium to produce fast neutrons which then get swallowed up in U^{238} and produce a nuclear reaction which spits out two neutrons, leaving U^{237} as the end product. Of course, some of the

U^{238} will fission, too, but a good number should produce U^{237}. Thus, Kimura's observation provided experimental confirmation for my theory as to what happened inside the superbomb. Naturally, I was elated that I had found the solution to a tough problem, just as a mystery story fan is delighted when he figures out who-did-it before the author tells all.

But my elation was short-lived as I turned to thinking through the implications of my discovery.

If two-thirds of the superbomb's punch came from cheap uranium, I calculated that this would be enough to spread a lethal contamination over eight thousand square miles. I felt that this was conservative for under bad weather conditions, or if an enemy deliberately sought to emphasize the radioactive peril, the fall-out could be worse. It must be remembered that at Bikini, as in all bomb tests, we detonate weapons under ideal conditions designed to minimize fall-out.

The late summer of 1954 found me sure of my facts. I had little doubt as to the nature of the bomb and its prodigious radioactivity. Yet these facts had not been revealed by the U.S. government. True, the Atomic Energy Commission had made a single press statement on March 31, 1954, two days after Admiral Lewis L. Strauss returned from the Pacific. But this statement was scarcely revealing. Nothing was said of the nature of the new bomb nor was there any hint of its revolutionary radioactivity. Admiral Strauss admitted that the wind had shifted and that there had been a fall-out on the *Lucky Dragon*. But with respect to what were obviously radiation injuries, Admiral Strauss had this to say: "Skin lesions observed are thought to be due to the chemical activity of the converted material in the coral rather than to radioactivity, since these lesions are said to be already healing." A most perplexing remark for the chairman of the AEC! One wonders whether or not the scientists told the Admiral what the superbomb really was or whether he understood their explanation. My own feeling is that the Admiral understood but was dictating a party line which Herblock summed up so well in a cartoon: he labeled the AEC the "Good News Commission."

Well, the superbomb was very bad news, indeed. Especially for the U.S.A. with its sprawling metropolitan areas so vulnerable to fall-out. I had been concerned with civil defense ever since I saw my first A-test. My mind had imprinted on it the grim transfer of the test to its effect upon an American city. Thus, I felt compelled to warn people about the nature of the new weapon development which compelled a drastic revision of all civil defense planning. I had been acting with the *Bulletin of the Atomic Scientists* as a civil defense editor, so it was natural for me to prepare an article called "Civil Defense Faces New Peril."

This article, appearing in the fall of 1954, spelled out the nature of radioactive fall-out. However, I carefully refrained from specifying the new nature of the superbomb. In so doing, I passed up a real news scoop which some editor would have headlined "H-Bomb Not an H-Bomb." In writing the article I knew that I was going out on a limb. I was quite sure that the AEC would gladly saw off that limb if it were too slender, i.e., if I did not have my facts straight. I waited anxiously to see how the Commission would respond.

The response was both puzzling and enlightening. On December 2, 1954, Dr. Willard F. Libby, newly appointed to the Commission, spoke out. Addressing the Washington Conference of Mayors, the solemn-visaged scientist delivered a highly technical talk on nuclear weapons. I doubt if many in the audience understood his jargon of fission-product fall-out, roentgens, curies and radioisotopes. Furthermore, he spoke of fall-out from A-bombs, whereas all the mayors had heard about thousandfold more powerful superbombs. I was puzzled that Dr. Libby should confine himself to old-fashioned A-bombs, but then I saw the light. His data were so chosen that the fall-out from an A-bomb was distributed over a small area of twenty square miles. I figured out that this would be about the same as Bikini Baker of 1946 vintage. Furthermore, it produced an average fall-out close to what I had calculated for the Bikini 1954 bomb, spread out over eight thousand square miles. You see, the superbomb behaved as a gigantic A-bomb. All you had to do was to scale up the effects of a small A-bomb to get data appropriate for a superbomb. I'm sure that's what Dr. Libby was doing, apparently trying hard to get the right data out in the open but bucking stiff resistance within the AEC.

Carefully, I checked all the data in Dr. Libby's speech. Things checked out fairly well, and, although I was still out on a limb, I felt that Dr. Libby had propped it up. In fact, he did more than that. His speech prompted me to re-examine something which I had not taken too seriously, namely, the persistence of the fall-out radioactivity. I knew how the dust had retained its radioactivity for more than two weeks on the *Lucky Dragon*. But I had not appreciated how small amounts of radioactivity can add up to significant totals day after day. It's somewhat like drinking cocktails—perhaps one or two a day. The amount in any one day is small, but if you add up a month's drinking the total alcohol is considerable. The difference between cocktails and fall-out is that you throw off the effect of a cocktail easily (this nonchalant assertion is made on my experience with about one cocktail per month). On the other hand, the human body remembers the effect of radioactivity. This memory is not perfect—there is some slippage, but nonetheless body cells bear the imprint of radiation and do not forget it readily. They add up the daily doses in a rather complicated and still not well-understood way.

The big break in the government's solid-front secrecy on fall-out came on February 15, 1955. On that day the Atomic Energy Commission disclosed: "About 7,000 square miles of territory downwind, was so contaminated that survival might have depended upon prompt evacuation of the area or upon taking shelter." At last the truth was out. But not quite all the way, for Admiral Strauss hedged: "The main radioactivity of fall-out decreases very rapidly with time—for the most part, within the first hours after the explosion." Furthermore, all AEC fall-out data were tied to a time period of the first thirty-six hours, clearly implying no long-term hazard. Moreover, the AEC statement on fall-out played down the hazard associated with breathing in or ingesting material from fall-out.

Persistence of fall-out radioactivity ranks with the

actual area contaminable with a single weapon as a radically different departure in weapon effectiveness. A high-explosive shell may explode but a few seconds later you can jump into the shell hole and be safe. With radioactivity we have a persistence in time which may deny occupation of territory. Let's see just what this means. Obviously, we must start with some assumptions about the size of the bomb, the extent of fall-out and so forth. I shall assume that the split atoms of uranium produced by an explosion equivalent to ten megatons of TNT are uniformly distributed over an area of ten thousand square miles. This is rather conservative, being somewhat less than the March 1, 1954, fall-out. Now let's see how the radioactive power fades away as time passes.

We must, of course, hark back to the roentgen as the measure of radioactivity, or more correctly as the measure of the dose received from the fall-out. If the bomb goes off at noon today and we start our measurements at 3 P.M. (this being the time of fall-out, say a hundred miles downwind), then we have the following schedule of fall-out persistence. From 3 P.M. until midnight, tonight, you would receive twelve hundred roentgens of radiation if you stood in the open. This would correspond to between two to three times the lethal amount of radiation; in other words, your goose would be cooked—extra well done. From midnight until tomorrow noon, you would receive an *additional* five hundred roentgens. Of course, this would be adding insult to injury if you had received twelve hundred roentgens already. But if you had been safely sheltered the first nine hours, you would then receive more than a lethal dose in the next twelve. In the period from noon, tomorrow, until midnight, we tally another 275 roentgens. Then 300 the next day; 125 the next, and 95 after that. A week later you would still have to face a total of 60 roentgens per day. So if you stayed sheltered a week you could stay out all during the eighth day without being injured.

This does mean that the radioactive "fire-power" had been lost after seven days. It would continue to emanate at a slower and slower but still significant rate. Score for the second week: a total of 280 roentgens. Then 160 the third week, 130 the fourth and so on, gradually getting less, but again by no means insignificant.

To my mind these facts add up to wholesale denial of thousands of square miles of area for weeks and even months. To survive, people would have to stay below deck or face the inevitable and grim consequences of radiation damage with all that it implies for the future.

An adequate civilian defense has to plan for survival against the primary effects of heat and blast as well as against the longer-lasting effects of radioactivity. This twofold requirement poses a dual dilemma since you really have to get out of town to be far enough away to survive the heat-blast punch of the superbomb; yet once evacuated to the countryside, you are out in the open exposed to radioactive fall-out. There is no cheap or easy solution to this nightmare for an effective civil defense will be both costly and difficult. In my opinion, shelters will have to be built on the periphery of each city so that city-dwellers may be evacuated to temporary safe lodging to weather the nuclear storm.

My "solution" to the civil defense quandary is, I believe, basically sound and practicable. But it is of multibillion-dollar dimension, and it will require considerable face-lifting of the profile of American cities and a drastic change in Congressional and public attitude before such a program can be started. In retrospect it seems a strange commentary that the United States, which developed the original A-bomb, has drifted along for more than a decade without a real civil defense. The great and continuing vulnerability of U.S. cities to nuclear attack constitutes a severe liability in an age of superweapons. The radically new feature of this age is that the United States, for the first time in its history, is terribly naked to attack and can be knocked out overnight. Thereafter, our population would have to shift for itself—the broken stubs of our cities would be uninhabitable as would much of the countryside.

As if this were not enough, we have yet to consider the problem of food contamination. Here we return to the Japanese fish market. Did "hot" fish continue to be brought in by Japanese ships? Not if we believe the AEC's official party line: "With respect to the stories concerning widespread contamination of tuna and other fish as a result of the test, the facts do not confirm them. The only contaminated fish discovered were those in the open hold of the Japanese trawler." To be fair to Admiral Strauss, he made this statement a month after the March 1st blast and thus might rightly have been uninformed, but he had a chance to clear the record on March 24, 1955, in testifying before

Senator Anderson's watchdog committee. The Admiral declared with respect to the fall-out statement: "It is interesting in rereading the statement to see that it does comport substantially with what we have since learned. That is to say there are no glaring inaccuracies in it. There are lacunae of course."

The lacunae, meaning, a few blank spaces in the statement, include the Japanese fishermen not suffering from radioactivity; radioactivity not persisting very long and only fish aboard the *Lucky Dragon* being contaminated.

Here are the facts about contaminated fish brought into Japan after the March first shot. From March 16 to April 30 nineteen boats were found to have contaminated fish. In all 213,000 pounds of fish were destroyed during this period. And ships fishing in southern waters reported radioactive catches as late as October of the same year.

Americans will be more interested in tuna fish meant for home consumption. In this connection I learned that there had been some commotion at a West Coast cannery. Upon checking with an official of the Food and Drug Administration, I found that the U.S. government had seized some contaminated fish about to be canned by a California concern. When I asked how radioactive the fish were, the answer was "insignificant," to which I replied, "What would that be in counts per minute?" The official then asked why I wanted to know, and when I told him I might want to write about it, he bristled. "I'm sorry I can't tell you. We had a meeting of people from the State Department, from the AEC, from the West Coast tuna industry and from our department. We decided that the information would be kept *confidential.*" We might call this the case of the confidential tuna fish. Actually, I am sure that these fish, if eaten, would not have been dangerous, but officials feared a near-panic such as occurred in Japan; so they invoked censorship. I am sure that the security laws of the U.S.A. were never designed to apply to tuna fish.

I have in my files stacks of data sent to me by Japanese scientists detailing their analyses of marine radioactivity. One of the most outstanding authorities on marine biology told me that the Japanese research in fish contamination is far better than ours. Many of the research reports I have at hand stress the importance of one element in the fall-out swallowed by the fish. It is strontium. The particular form of strontium, found as a split uranium atom, is strontium-90. It is long-lived, having a half-life of twenty-eight years. Its extreme toxicity in man is due to a combination of factors. Chemically, it resembles calcium, and once ingested it seeks out the bone as its resting place. Therefore it is excreted very slowly from the body. Because it lays down in the bone it is strategically located to cause radiation damage to blood-forming cells. A very small amount of it (actually so small as to be meaningless to the average person) can produce bone tumors in human beings.

Thus, we have a real pertinent question to ask the Atomic Energy Commission. Specifically, how dangerous is radioactive strontium in fall-out? Naturally, we mean in the region of heavy fall-out close to where a bomb is detonated. The official AEC answer is oblique. Instead of a straightforward statement, the Commission concerned itself with evaluating the danger from radiostrontium in global fall-out. In other words, it worried about how much strontium fell on the U.S.A. from its bomb-testing program. It concluded: "The amount of radiostrontium now present in the soil as a result of all nuclear explosions to date would have to be increased many thousand times before any effect on humans would be noticeable." Here is the rub. Fall-out from the present bomb tests goes to the ends of the earth. In fact, the 1955 expedition to the Antarctic found strontium there. We've tested only a few of the supers, and the area of fall-out is two hundred million square miles. If you take a single superbomb and restrict the fall-out to ten thousand square miles, then the amount of fall-out *will be* many thousands of times greater than what it is now. That's why some scientists are deeply worried over the AEC's apparently cheery attitude on the strontium hazard.

This intense worry has communicated itself to at least one of the Commissioners in the AEC. Thomas E. Murray, industrialist-engineer, has spoken out: "We know that there is a limit to the amount of this strontium that the human body can absorb without harmful effects. Beyond that limit danger lies, and even death." He went on to underline this point: "This is a crucial point to remember when there is talk of an all-out-nuclear war."

The limit of danger for radioactive strontium is much in dispute, but the AEC has set a Maximum Permissible Amount (MPA) retained in the human body as one-millionth of a curie unit. The latter, however, is meant to apply to healthy adults working in AEC installations under strict supervision and control. Project Sunshine experts have estimated that the radioactive fall-out from our superbomb tests of 1954 and those of the Soviets in 1955 will eventually lead to a deposition in the bones of earth-dwellers to the extent of 1 or 2 per cent of an MPA. This takes no account of bombs which will be tested in the future, and if one makes a reasonable guess about the next decade of the arms race, then one concludes that within the next fifteen years people all over the globe will begin to approach an MPA unit of radiostrontium taken into their bones from milk, vegetables and foodstuff which is dusted by the fall-out. These estimates are based upon actual measurements made by Project Sunshine personnel, using human bones made available from hospitals.

Experts within the AEC are within their authority when they lay down rules for strontium MPA's for AEC workers. However, it is completely misleading to apply these same rules to all of the world's population including children, the infirm and those who by some vagary of nature are more sensitive to radiation damage. It must be emphasized that radiostrontium is the world's most toxic poison, one teaspoonful of which contains an MPA dose for every person on earth. That is, an MPA unit of AEC definition. Actually, there is no MPA unit for a world population, but health physicists agree that it should be at least ten and probably one hundred times less than the AEC's MPA value. My own view is that we should argue for a wide margin of safety when the health of everyone on the planet is at stake.

Outbursts of candor from the Commission are rare, but those of Mr. Murray do indicate internal dissension at a high level in our atomic agency. In general, the public information policy of the AEC is to release data only after the story has been forced out through the efforts of the press. This was true in the case of fall-out, where the AEC waited almost a full year before revealing what had happened before dawn on March 1, 1954. That was a fateful day for humanity. But for the accident of the *Lucky Dragon* and an errant, misbehaving wind, the world might still be in ignorance of the revolutionary phenomena of radioactive fall-out.

chapter 8

SOVIETS, SPIES AND SUPER

Radioactive fall-out of invisible but telltale particles is not limited to U.S. bomb tests. The Soviets, too, are confronted with the troublesome rain-out of bomb clouds, and for them it is an even more serious problem than for us. After all, we have the Eniwetok Proving Grounds in the far Pacific, where, except for accidents like those just described, the fall-out drops into the Pacific Ocean. Russian tests, however, take place over a continental land mass, and the danger of contamination is very severe.

Proving Grounds are very expensive to maintain, and not even with the vast real estate of Siberia can the Soviets write off chunks of territory measured in thousands of square miles. Yet this would be almost sure to happen if the Soviets tested multimegaton bombs close to the earth's surface. That is one reason why the Soviets are known to have preferred to detonate some of their high-power bombs at high altitude. As long as the bomb's fireball does not touch the earth, the danger of intense local fall-out is minimized.

However, not even the secretive Soviets can keep their tests free from the prying eyes of the West. By this I do not mean that we have agents in their Proving Grounds. Our "prying" is done remotely and in a most unconventional manner. Instead of depending upon spies, we now rely upon scientists and instruments. The United States organized a special Long Range

Detection Project late in 1947 for the sole purpose of ferreting out news of Soviet atomic tests. This project, fathered initially by our Intelligence Agency, was almost stillborn and has had a rather hectic history. Originally our intelligence experts treated it as such an ultrasecret affair that scientists were excluded from the very project which only they could make successful. The man responsible for yanking the work out of its paralysis was the venerable Dr. Vannevar Bush, head of the Carnegie Institution and, at the time, chairman of the Research and Development Board in the Defense Department. Dr. Bush with his direct New England bluntness and courage stepped in and completely reorganized the LRD project (I had called it *Project Bunyan* in my files, but the Air Force felt the name might become odorous).

Dr. Bush's shake-up of the detection program gave it new priority, and Air Force technicians set about exploring how new instruments might be developed for the purpose of tracking down a bomb detonation somewhere in Siberia. An obvious approach was to use Geiger counters to measure airborne radioactive remnants of the explosion. Another method was to listen for the shock wave with supersensitive seismographs or to feel the change in atmospheric pressure with ultraprecise microbarographs. Other more bizarre methods suggested themselves, for example, trying to catch the splash of light reflected from the moon by the burst of a Siberian bomb.

The LRD program was urgently needed if it was to be tuned up in time to monitor our *Sandstone* series of bangs in the Pacific. Our own nuclear tests could be used to calibrate the detection net to see how effectively it performed. The Air Force, which had been given the job by Vannevar Bush, got nowhere fast, and it became quite apparent that our *Sandstone* tests would never be picked up in time. Again, acting with characteristic courage, Dr. Bush took a big stick approach to the problem. This time, he succeeded in placing one of his own trusted men, mild-looking but dynamic Dr. Ellis Johnson, at the top command of the scientific work. The forty-two-year-old, pudgy Ph.D. used a bare knuckles approach to his work and soon had a number of Air Force generals gasping. I remember that one officer at Wright Field used the most profane language and threatened to personally kick Ellis Johnson all the way out to the Main Gate. What Dr. Johnson did was to slam ahead and get the work done; he left Air Force protocol and red tape for others to worry about. Thanks to his sledge-hammer activities, we were successful in detecting our own nuclear tests. The LRD system worked. But the free-wheeling Dr. Johnson was more than the Air Force could stand, so Dr. Bush adroitly switched him to another post.

Very few people around the Pentagon at the time seemed to feel any great sense of urgency about detecting the first Soviet A-bomb. Certainly, this was even more true in the headquarters of the AEC across the Potomac. The general impression was that it would take the Soviets a long time to catch up with us.

In 1945 Dr. Karl Compton sat in on a conference with Fermi, Oppenheimer, Ernest Lawrence and his brother, Arthur Compton. They talked about how soon the Soviets might have the A-bomb and to quote the late Karl Compton: "We came to the very rough estimate that it would require Russia a minimum of 5 years and a maximum of 20 and probably 10 to produce an atomic bomb." General Groves told Congress it would take fifteen or twenty years—"if then."

Shortly after these top bomb experts made their estimate, another group of scientists made an independent estimate. These men were the scientific advisors to the non-Soviet delegations to the United Nations. Early in 1946 they gathered together quite informally and pooled their thinking on the subject. I shall tabulate their estimates alongside the ones just given:

	U.S. estimate	UN estimate
Earliest possible date:	1950	1947
Most probable date:	1955	1949
Latest date:	1965	1951

As events turned out, the UN advisors, with no secret knowledge about the bomb, hit the date right on the nose; whereas the top U.S. experts were way off. To be fair to the U.S. estimates, they were later revised downward, but even so in the summer of 1949 the Central Intelligence Agency was estimating that the first Soviet nuclear explosion would occur in the winter of 1951-52.

The LRD project, which Ellis Johnson had successfully tuned up in 1948, did not have long to wait for news of a Soviet test. In August of the next year, Air Force planes, flying above the continental U.S.A., brought down to earth samples of air collected at high altitude. Preliminary survey of these samples revealed that they were radioactive beyond what one normally obtains in the atmosphere. The next step in this *Operation Vermont* was to be sure that the radioactivity was of bomb origin. The "hot" sample was rushed to a radiochemical laboratory, specially designated for this purpose, and tests soon proved that the sample contained split atoms of plutonium. There could be no doubt about it—the Soviets had set off a nuclear weapon.

Vannevar Bush headed up a small task force of scientists who analyzed the data thoroughly. There could be no question now, for additional tests confirmed the first one. President Truman was personally briefed by the scientists and they were momentarily persuasive for on September 23, 1949, he announced, "We have evidence that within recent weeks an atomic explosion occurred in the U.S.S.R."

Why had the U.S. experts been so wrong and the UN non-experts so right? First, I hasten to add that there were a number of U.S. experts, like Leo Szilard, who were right, but, in general, the U.S. scientists highest in government circles were the ones who set such a long-time scale for the Soviet A-project. Vannevar Bush, himself, suffered the crowning ignominy of publishing his book *Modern Arms and Free Men* just after the news of the Soviet test hit the newspapers. His book contained a very long-range estimate of Soviet capability in the nuclear field. I believe that in all fairness U.S. scientists were too close to the bomb to assess it properly. They saw all the difficulties too clearly. And one must not forget the element of national ego involved. The longer it took for the Soviets to master the atomic art, the greater would be the prestige of U.S. scientists at home.

Then the news broke that the British had apprehended one Dr. Klaus Fuchs, formerly in the top echelon at Los Alamos. Bewildered and disillusioned, Fuchs confessed that he had transmitted vital A-secrets to the Soviets. Almost everyone jumped to the conclusion that "Dr. Fuchs gave the A-bomb to the Soviets." Now, it is certainly true that Fuchs turned over accurate data to the Soviets. We know that he was familiar with the details of the Oak Ridge processes. Furthermore, Fuchs wrote the Los Alamos *Handbook on Implosion Technique.* But there is a vast difference between paper plans and producing plants. Dr. James Beckerley, director of the AEC's division dealing with secrecy, pointed out: "A spy's reports may have told Soviet technicians how an atomic weapon operated, but the reports did not build the weapon nor the complex fissionable material production plants needed to supply nuclear explosives."

How then do we explain the unexpectedly early Soviet success with Joe I—their first A-bomb? Remembering, of course, that it was not *early* except to U.S. experts. On this point top-ranking physicist James Beckerley had this to say (after he left government circles): "Personally, I believe that it was primarily through the efforts of Soviet scientists and engineers, backed up by a ruthless totalitarian resolve to dominate the world, that the U.S.S.R. became armed with fission weapons as early as 1949."

Let's look into the two areas where Dr. Fuchs could

have helped the Soviets the most. First, he gave them data on Oak Ridge production processes. I would like to emphasize two points in this regard. One, the Joe I weapon tested by the Soviets used Hanford production type bomb material (plutonium) rather than that which comes from Oak Ridge production plants. Two, plans for a production plant are only a small part of the whole. The really big job during the war was to erect the vast production plants at Oak Ridge and Hanford; this was more a secret of American industry than of science. Second, Dr. Fuchs did pass on to the Soviets data on bomb construction. But remember in our discussion of the first U.S. bomb, I emphasized that Los Alamos experts were ready to test well before the bomb stuff arrived from the production plants.

All of this adds up to the fact that the real task the Soviets faced in making the bomb was primarily one of heavy industry and production. Fanatic emphasis in U.S.A. upon atomic secrecy obscured the fact that the Soviets had perfectly good scientists who could find the answers for themselves. No law of nature makes science different on either side of the Iron Curtain. Furthermore, the big secret about the bomb—that you could make one—vanished in the mushroom cloud at Hiroshima.

The Fuchs affair, it seems to me, is not fully explained today. Why was it that he remained undiscovered for so long? Who pointed the finger that revealed his monumental betrayal? To my knowledge, it has been universally assumed that expert FBI and British sleuthing ran Fuchs down, but is it not possible that he was double-crossed? Recall the circumstances at the time; Fuchs no longer had access to secret data, he had, in fact, evidenced a change of heart toward the Soviets. Moreover, the British and U.S. were on the verge of resuming co-operation in atomic development. Supposing the Soviets wished to drive a wedge between the U.S. and the U.K., what better wedge could be invented than one Klaus Fuchs? He could have been "fingered" through a double agent without arousing suspicion. Clearly, in terms of the results, the Soviets could not have devised a better way of splitting the allies in the area of the atom.

But such wedge-driving requires a high degree of sophistication. Were the Soviets smart enough to use Fuchs as a divisive force? I cannot prove the point, but in the case of Bruno Pontecorvo, who defected to the Soviets, the evidence seems solid. Pontecorvo could not rank with Fuchs in scientific importance, but on the front page of newspapers a scientist's credentials are never carefully examined, especially if he is accused of treachery. Pontecorvo was seized upon by spy-conscious columnists as being the H-bomb counterpart to Fuchs. The Soviet government maintained a stony silence about the whereabouts of Pontecorvo and never even admitted that he was in the Soviet Union. Then, one day, the Soviets trotted out Pontecorvo and exposed him to a press conference in Moscow. It so happened that, the very same day, a high British official landed in New York City to try to reestablish U.S.–U.K. co-operation in atomic development. The effect of Pontecorvo's sudden materialization was to squash any hopes that such transatlantic agreement on the atom would be resumed. I believe that the Soviet strategy with respect to Pontecorvo makes my speculation about Fuchs quite plausible.

Even after the Fuchs affair, Americans persisted in underestimating the Soviets. In fact, to many the treachery of Fuchs confirmed their suspicions that the Soviets were so badly off in science that they were forced to rely upon espionage. Somehow or other, Americans could not dissociate themselves from the notion that another country could duplicate our feat in making an A-bomb. Mr. Truman must be counted among the many for, just after he left office in 1953, the former President made the startling announcement: "I am not convinced Russia has the [atomic] bomb. . . . I am not convinced the Russians have achieved the know-how to put the complicated mechanism together to make an A-bomb work, I am not convinced they have the bomb."

Mind you, this Doubting Harry statement emerged after the Soviets had detonated additional fission bombs in 1951, while Mr. Truman was still President. Our LRD project, then reclassified as AFOAT-1, had developed even better methods of sniffing the air and had collected incontestible evidence about the Siberian nuclear shots. Moreover, the data indicated that the Soviets were proceeding on an accelerated program in weapon development. Newly inaugurated President Eisenhower refuted Mr. Truman when he referred to "incontrovertible evidence" of the Soviet A-bomb in his February 2, 1953, State of the Union address.

General Leslie R. Groves, who had previously estimated it would take the Soviets "20 years, if then" to get their first A-bomb, stepped into the argument and muddied the water. "All we know," asserted Groves, "is there were indications of nuclear explosions in Russia. That does not prove that they have the bomb in workable form." Tacking along this line, the *New York Times* captioned an article "Russia Has an A-Bomb but How Good Is It?" The usually objective *Times* has printed stories on nuclear weapons which are in marked contrast with the excellent reporting of other news.

This background of skepticism scarcely prepared the U.S.A. for Malenkov's boasting of August 8, 1953, that "the United States no longer has a monopoly of the hydrogen bomb." Official Washington greeted this news with disbelief, yet on August 20 the Atomic Energy Commission was forced to admit: "The Soviet Union conducted an atomic test on the morning of August 12. Certain information to this effect came into our hands that night. Subsequent information on the subject indicates that this test involved both fission and thermonuclear reactions."

The United States had tested its first so-called H-bomb on November 1, 1952, some seven years after its first A-bomb. The Soviet gap between their first A-weapon and their H-bomb was almost exactly four years. There could be no question but that the Soviets were driving ahead relentlessly in nuclear development. As a postcript to the August thermonuclear test, they added a series of A-tests in the fall of 1953. A year later they conducted an extensive series of nuclear tests, including a total of at least seven detonations in the fall of 1954. It is difficult to say where one test series left off and the next began, for the Siberian shots then came quite regularly throughout 1955 and thereafter.

Nikita Khrushchev, while touring southeast Asia with his comrade Bulganin, made the next Soviet announcement of an H-weapon. On November 26, 1955, on a good-will mission in Bangalore, India, Khrushchev revealed that the Soviets had detonated a megaton weapon at high altitude in order to minimize radioactive fall-out. There was much speculation about how the Soviets had managed to make a high-altitude burst, and strangely enough no one seemed to point to the most obvious way. The simplest manner for a high burst is to put the bomb in a remote-controlled aircraft, fly it on a predetermined course and then detonate either by a Mother-to-Drone plane relay or by ground radio beacon. Other methods of delivering the bomb involve very considerable difficulties for the bomber. A straight air drop is questionable, for the bomber would have to be able to get out of the way in time. A delayed air drop (retardation by finning) is probably the method used by the U.S. Air Force in its May 21, 1956, air drop which went wide of its mark by 3½ miles. An obvious method of delivery is to package the bomb as the warhead for a missile—a good way, providing you have the missile.

It was on another good-will tour that the brawny, excitable Khrushchev did some more chest-beating. This time it was England and the date was April 23, 1956. "I am quite sure," bragged the Soviet leader, "that we will have a guided missile with a hydrogen bomb that can fall anywhere in the world." We shall have more to say about this "ultimate weapon" later, but for the moment let us keep focused on the bomb.

Did the Soviets have Super? Their first test on August 12, 1953, was described by AEC chairman Strauss as "a weapon or device of yield well beyond the range of regular fission weapons and deriving part of its force from the fusion of light elements." However, Super produces most of its bang from the fission of heavy elements—either natural uranium or thorium. So, the Admiral's statement does not clarify the issue. In fact, the Atomic Energy Commission has never really owned up to the nature of the superbomb.

The AEC did spill the beans about the nature of the superbomb in June of 1955, but the spilling operation was so coy that it was a kind of legerdemain. The date was June 3 and the occasion was an Alumni Reunion honoring Dr. Willard F. Libby, who had left the University of Chicago faculty to become an Atomic Energy Commissioner. Speaking before his old friends, Dr. Libby proceeded to give a highly technical exposition of radioactive fall-out. Probably only a few of his audience caught the significance of a single sentence: "Let us follow a nuclear explosion releasing 10 megatons of fission energy or 1,100 pounds of fission products."

The beans were out in the open, but the press apparently did not see them. That is, with one exception, for the *New York Times* reporter, Anthony Leviero, spotted them and concluded in a front-page article on June 13: "Dr. Libby referred to a 10,000,000-ton weapon that released energy by fission rather than fusion. This indicated that ordinary, cheap Uranium-238 was the major explosive content and was responsible for fall-out over a vast area." Leviero could obtain no comment from the AEC on the superbomb or U-bomb. It had been in the news all spring and, in fact, Admiral Strauss was queried about it on a TV program on April 3, 1955:

Question: Does the United States have the "U" bomb?

Admiral Strauss: I don't know what is meant by the "U" bomb. I have seen some pieces by columnists using that expression, but so far as I am aware, there is no such weapon.

Judging from Admiral Strauss's answer and Dr. Libby's speech, there seems to be kind of a shell game being played at a high level in the Atomic Energy Commission. Now you see it; now you don't. The gentlemen of the press didn't catch up again with the AEC members until the fall of 1955, when the AEC held one of its rare press conferences. A reporter asked a direct question about the U-bomb and got a "No comment" answer from Dr. Libby. Yet, there can be only one interpretation of Dr. Libby's speech of June 3, 1955. The superbomb must derive the lion's share of its punch from ordinary cheap uranium. The line of argument we followed in tracing the origin of the radioactivity in the preceding chapter makes this quite clear. Why, then, the curious policy of the AEC in refusing comment on what everyone else seems to know?

Everyone else in this case apparently does not include William L. Laurence, science writer for the *New York Times*. Commenting upon the detonation of the first air-dropped U.S. superbomb (May 21, 1956) Laurence wrote that the H-bomb was a true fusion or thermonuclear weapon, and scoffed at the "so-called fission-fusion-fission" bomb. Without giving any explanation, he went on:

This lays to rest some fantastic speculations that the hydrogen bomb was not actually a fusion bomb, but rather a so-called fission-fusion-fission device, in which some 80 per cent of the explosive force is derived not from fusion but rather from the fission of the otherwise non-fissionable and most abundant form of uranium, namely, Uranium–238.

The so-called fission-fusion-fission bomb, therefore, must henceforth be known as "the fission-fusion-fission-fiction" bomb.

Thus, within one year, the *New York Times* served up two completely different versions of the same story, one by Tony Leviero and the other by William Laurence; no explanation of the contradictory reporting has yet been given to the *Times* readers. And, of course, the Atomic Energy Commission offered no comment.

Did the AEC really think that the Soviets did not have Super or were unaware of the nature of the fission-fusion-fission bomb? Perhaps the best name to give to this so-called hydrogen bomb or thermonuclear weapon is "compound fission." But since the name H-bomb is so fixed in the public mind, we will continue using the term without bothering to qualify it as "so-called." Any doubts which the AEC entertained should have been dissipated by the 1955-1956 Soviet tests which caused a revealing fall-out. The Soviets had Super! The latter was identified by Japanese scientists, who are turning out to be the middlemen in the Super contest between the East and the West.

The explanation for the AEC's reluctance to admit the facts about the revolutionary new Super is, in my opinion, to be found in the personalities of government officials. Secretary of Defense Charles E. Wilson is known for his view that you should not scare the American people to death. Budget-balancers are disturbed that revelation of the basic facts would almost automatically require further defense expenditures and upset the budget. And last, but by no means least, is Admiral Lewis L. Strauss, whose views on secrecy have never been secret.

"Too little security," asserts the Admiral, "when it is realized, is beyond correction. It is too late by then. There is no use having doors on stables—not to mention locks, after the horse is stolen." Notice the tacit assumption that an enemy would have to steal in order to possess a weapon. Basic to those who cling to the straws of secrecy is an overwhelming ego; in this case a national pride that only one country is capable of developing weapons.

As for revealing the nature of the U.S. stockpile, Admiral Strauss is adamant. Commenting on this heretical thought, the Admiral said: "To the public, it could scarcely be anything but a number, revealing, in itself, neither that it was sufficient nor too large nor too small." In other words, trust Father for he knows best. "The number *would be* significant—fatally significant, however, in another quarter, that is to say, in the planning staff of a potential enemy. It would be a quixotic and short-lived commander who signalled his enemy how many rounds he had in his locker," is the final argument advanced by the AEC chairman. But let's look at this one a little closer. A commander caught with too few rounds in his locker might indeed succumb quickly, but we have long since passed the Mother Hubbard stage in stockpiling nuclear weapons. A commander with a locker bulging with weapons is less likely to be attacked *if* the enemy knows the stockpile. Therefore, it makes sense to advertise your striking power if you wish it to be a deterrent. Otherwise, an enemy might miscalculate.

I wonder, however, quite apart from the fact that spy-minded men never really wake up to reality, if there is not a deeper motivation behind the reluctance of the AEC to admit the radical change in nuclear weaponry. The AEC is a giant business with operating expenses running to more than two billion dollars per year—as much as the total wartime investment in the original A-bomb. The bulk of these funds go into producing bomb material at the huge Oak Ridge and Hanford type plants, which turn out ten-thousand-dollar per pound "nuke" material. Superbombs wring their might principally from ordinary uranium or even the waste material from Oak Ridge. Could it be that AEC officials fear that revelation of the facts would shrink the agency to smaller dimensions? Do they fear that the new billion-dollar plants at Savannah River; Portsmouth, Ohio; and Paducah, Kentucky, will become "white elephants"?

The time is long overdue for the bulk of atomic activities to be brought out from the penumbra of secrecy and exposed to the light of day. The Atomic

Energy Commission must emerge from its decade-long enchantment with secrecy and face up to the fact that its massive preoccupation with keeping secrets has not impeded Soviet development of A-bombs or Supers.

Uranium fission in the superbomb is the source of the radioactive fall-out or "dirty" effect of the bomb. The dirtiness of a megaton weapon depends upon the ratio of fission to fusion energy release. *Operation Redwing,* the U.S. Pacific tests in 1956, demonstrated weapons with "reduced fall-out." This means cleaner experimental weapons were tested in which fusion predominated over fission. This is a logical test development where the fall-out is undesirable. But it does not mean that dirty bomb will be replaced by a clean bomb as a military weapon.

As we have emphasized, radioactive fall-out maximizes the terror effect of the superbomb. It makes for a weapon which can stray off target and still hit with fall-out over thousands of square miles. The dirtiness of the bomb is a military advantage and is not likely to be sacrificed in war.

War is a dirty business and science has not made it less so.

chapter 9

STRATEGY AND WORLD PEACE

Both the U.S.A. and the U.S.S.R. possess sizable stockpiles of superweapons, the power of which is quite sufficient to devastate a continental land mass. This is the radically new feature of the arms race, which, if understood, revolutionizes the age-old art of war.

Poetic Dr. Oppenheimer, renowned for his phrasemaking, analyzed the situation in a colorful way. "We may anticipate a state of affairs," the former Los Alamos chief wrote in *Foreign Affairs,* "in which two Great Powers will each be in a position to put an end to the civilization and life of the other, though not without risking its own. We may be likened to two scorpions in a bottle, each capable of killing the other, but only at the risk of his own life."

Oppenheimer then made the understatement of the decade when he pointed out: "This prospect does not tend to make for serenity." He then stressed three all-important factors in the international situation: the hostility and power of the Soviets, the perilous unity of the alliance arrayed against the Soviets and, finally, the increasing peril of the atom.

President Dwight D. Eisenhower pointed to the same situation in terms of "two atomic colossi . . . doomed malevolently to eye each other indefinitely across a trembling world." And the great Sir Winston Churchill enunciated what was to become the guiding principle of the Cold War—"peace through mutual terror."

The foundation stone of national security in the age of superbombs was to be the mutual power of annihilation. As long as both sides held this power in unquestioned capability, then it was reasoned that neither one would strike first. Each would be deterred by the lethality of the other's Sunday punch. This policy did not emerge full-blown immediately after the war, but grew up gradually as the postwar international situation solidified and as the Soviets graduated to atomic arms. During the early postwar years the United States depended upon its atomic monopoly to keep the peace, although it did make some overtures through the United Nations to negotiate on the international control of atomic energy.

There is very little need to disinter the facts about the UN proposals which began in 1946 and continued deadlocked until eight years later. Quite clearly, the proposals were unacceptable to the Soviets who refused to negotiate as an atomic-have-not power. Even after the Russians broke our atomic monopoly, they perpetuated the deadlock in the UN disarmament conferences, looking toward the day when their own stockpile of nuclear weapons would approach parity with ours. It was quite obvious early in the game that the Soviets would not shift their stance in the UN until they were in a position to negotiate from strength.

A change was reflected in Soviet attitudes in the UN meetings in the spring of 1954. Up to that time representatives like Gromyko and Malik had repeated *ad nauseam* the thesis that the bomb should be banned.

But at no time did the Soviets retreat from their contention that the big atomic stick would first have to be laid aside before inspection of sovereign territory would be considered. This, naturally, would play right into the Soviet hand, for once nuclear weapons were ruled out then the superior conventional military arms of the U.S.S.R. would win out. Then, too, the Soviets undoubtedly perceived that the U.S. Senate would scarcely be enthusiastic about accepting terms which put the U.S. at a disadvantage.

In retrospect, one shudders at what might and probably would have happened, had the Soviets elected to accept our U.N. proposals. The U.S. Senate would probably have refused to agree to the plan, and the U.S.A. would then have been in the position of a warmonger or, at the very least, not a seeker of peace. And such was the purpose of much Soviet propaganda with regard to the atom. Skilled psychological warfare experts in the Kremlin dreamed up all sorts of angles to put the U.S. in a bad light. The Communist Radio in China pounded into people's eardrums the chant: "The U.S. had the A-bomb but would not use it against Germany. The A-bomb was reserved for use against the yellow race." At the same time the Soviets boasted of their peaceful use of the atom and harangued against the purely military uses which the Western world found for atomic energy.

The stiff back of Soviet unwillingness to negotiate on disarmament appeared to bend in 1954 when Andrei Vishinsky retreated from the previous Soviet stand on disarmament by discreet stages. Moreover, there appeared tentative signs that the Soviets might be willing to co-operate with other nations in the peacetime development of atomic energy. Things bogged down again, however, and it was not until May 10, 1955, when the U.S.S.R. broke the deadlock by proposing an inspection system and, at the same time, backing down from its rigid policy of banning the bomb without qualification. The May 10 proposals contained a good portion of realism but an unassessable amount of sincerity. Were the Soviets seriously proposing to let international inspectors penetrate the Iron Curtain? The Kremlin's policies shifted after Stalin's death, but no one could predict what lurked behind the inscrutable smiles of Premier Nikolai Bulganin and Party Chief Nikita Khrushchev.

The men in the Kremlin advanced proposals which were based upon the reality of stockpiles and super-bombs. They recognized that so much "nuke" material was above ground that it would be all but impossible to devise an accounting system which would keep perfect score on all the bomb stuff. With the prodigious power of the superbomb and its small investment in expensive "nuke" material, it would be too easy for a ruthless nation to conceal a few dozen bombs. The Soviets acknowledged the existence of "tension and distrust" in the world and an unwillingness to dissolve sovereignty; accordingly, they proposed what we may call an alarm system. This proposed spotting inspectors at ports, rail hubs and airdromes where preparations for war might be detected. What this might provide would be insurance against surprise attack. Nations of the world were not likely to forget the smiles of the Japanese before Pearl Harbor. The possibility of a thermonuclear Pearl Harbor has always remained uppermost in the minds of our nation's planners.

President Eisenhower reopened the inspection situation following the Soviet overture by proposing aerial surveillance; the plan being widely called his "open skies" proposal. This photoreconnaissance method of inspecting a nation's surface, made at the Geneva talks in the summer of 1955, was really a resurrection of schemes which originated in 1946, but, coming at a new stage in Soviet-American relations, it was heralded as a solution to the problem of international control. In reality, it was a foot-in-the-door step and merely kept the door open to further talks. The plan called for mutual overflights of U.S.A. and U.S.S.R. by each other's patrol aircraft. Information gained by scrutiny of aerial photographs might point to unusual surface activity such as might precede the outbreak of a war. What few Americans seemed to understand was that this plan would provide the U.S. with far more useful data than it would give the Soviets. Our nation is already quite open, whereas the interior of the U.S.S.R. is significantly denied to U.S. inspection. Any inspection plan submitted to the Soviets must be based upon a system of incentives which will prove attractive to the Soviets.

The basic objection which the Soviets have to any real inspection plan is that it will violate their sovereignty. Will the rulers of that country ever agree to a plan which would allow an international inspectorate to roam freely throughout the land? Certain concessions have been made in the past few years which permit freer penetration of the Iron Curtain than in the past, but large areas and many specific installations are still marked "Off limits." The Russian system of subjugation is in large measure predicated upon maintaining its isolation from the rest of the world. If the men in the Kremlin decide to open up their land to unrestricted travel, it will mark a drastic change in policy for which there is little precedent. The hopeful content of the situation is that there have been marked changes in the Soviet attitude in recent years and a measure of relaxation of internal controls. One might therefore hope that as time passes even greater changes might occur which would make an inspection plan more feasible.

However, the world is still swept along in the maelstrom of an armament race and there is little sign of a letup. Our present security is based upon the principle of deterrence, i.e., upon the application of military strength. Since this is the case, let us consider how this principle works and how it may be expected to apply in the future.

We can return to our scorpions and colossi to illustrate the principle. Whichever situation you prefer, scorpions in a bottle or giants armed with big sticks, makes little difference. The essential feature of each situation is that two forces of mutually lethal power are directly opposed within line of sight. Each colossus, to concentrate on President Eisenhower's language, is assumed to be intelligent so that he comprehends the other's power. Each is deterred from striking the other because of fear that he will, himself, be destroyed.

Nations are colossal, but I believe that it is illuminating to consider the actual situation rather than the personification of it. There are very real differences between two nations and two giants.

For one thing, the U.S. and the U.S.S.R. are not in line of sight. They are separated by a vast gulf of several thousand miles, and in addition each maintains tight secrecy of many aspects of national defense. Thus, the weapons are not in direct view. In fact, each nation must rely upon complex intelligence systems to appraise its opponent's military posture. As we have already seen, this appraisal in the case of Soviet atomic capability has been far from accurate. Thus, if one intends to adhere strictly to the principle of mutual terror, one should reveal many (but not all) aspects of deterrent power. If you really believe in deterrence, then you should advertise your power to deter so that the enemy will not make the mistake of underestimating your power. This does not mean "rattling the bomb," for it is comparatively easy to supply information to enemy intelligence without fanfare.

Perhaps we should hasten to interject in our contrast between colossus to colossus and the actual U.S.-U.S.S.R. situation that we must assume rationality. If either side were governed by irrationality, then all bets would be off—peace through mutual terror would be a dangerous delusion. It is discomfiting to recall that many wars have been precipitated by irrational acts or have witnessed climatic convulsions of irrationality. One would scarcely enjoy any reliance based upon deterring a Hitler or a Stalin.

To consider some other aspects of the differences between giants and nations, we must emphasize that a giant's big stick is an obvious and unchanging instrument of destruction. Modern weapons systems, on the other hand, constantly obsolesce and must be rejuvenated with new and more costly weapons and weapons carriers. The nature of the superexplosives which have been developed is such that each side may be viewed as "saturated"; each may continue to stockpile more and more bombs, but the means for mutual extinction, indeed, for continental destruction, is already at hand.

What is all-important now is the means of delivering nuclear destruction to targets situated thousands of miles away from home territory. Distance is immensely significant for it determines the nature of the delivery system. A bomber which need only deliver its payload over a range of a thousand miles is vastly different in structure and performance (and cost!) from an intercontinental bomber like the B-52. This is why the United States has put so much stress upon the development of overseas close-in bases from which B-47 jet bombers may operate. The shorter the range of the aircraft, the better will be its performance over the target. Higher terminal speed will mean fewer losses to enemy interceptor devices.

The point I am driving at is simply this: peace through mutual terror is a delicately balanced affair. If at any time our own strategic striking force should deteriorate, or if the enemy should come to the conclusion that our offense was inferior to his defense, then he might not be deterred from launching the first blow. This first blow might be a blitz attack upon the heartland of the U.S.A., although I am inclined to believe that it is more likely that the Soviets would aggress elsewhere in a munching operation designed to gobble up peripheral areas. Now the point to underline here is that the United States must maintain a strong strategic deterrent power at all times. Furthermore, the Soviet Union should never be kept in doubt about the power or the conditions under which it would be invoked.

When physicists analyze a problem involving equilibrium of forces, they put great stress upon "stability condition." Applied to our problem of equilibrium of atomic-delivery power, we must analyze under what conditions reliance upon peace through mutual fear would be stable. It seems to me that over-all the situation has the stability of an egg balanced on its most pointed end. It is a precarious balance, but since it is the best we have, we must do everything we can to keep the egg from toppling over.

Our analysis of strategic deterrence has overlooked a very relevant fact. Even during the days of our atomic monopoly we did not deter the Soviets from aggressing. True, no world war erupted in the face of the A-bomb, but the Soviets appropriated vast territories when they were either a have-not or a have-little nation with respect to nuclear weapons. Korea was overrun under the very shadow of our A-bomb.

Strategic deterrence is not enough; it must be supplemented with additional forces to deter local wars of the Korean type. Here the United States is presented with a perplexing dilemma. The Soviet world commands an impressive superiority in conventional arms and manpower with which local wars are fought. Our

Defense Department has concluded that it would drive the nation to the edge of bankruptcy if it were to demand a force in-being of men, planes, ships and armor capable of meeting Soviet force on an equal footing. The New Look in national defense planning, therefore, sought alternatives to relieve this dilemma and to provide a more complete system of deterrence. Something new was needed to beef up the NATO defenses in western Europe as well as to counter aggression in places such as Indo-China and Formosa.

It was probably inevitable that the answer to this quest would be found in the atomic arsenal. The Army needed more fire-power and less manpower. Could not the atomic bomb be packaged to fit into an artillery piece or as a warhead for a battlefield missile? We know the answer, of course, since we have already discussed the low end of the nuclear family of weapons. A single atomic shell could substitute for thousands of ordinary artillery shells. A single atomic missile, like Honest John, could deliver the punch farther behind the front line and substitute for a hundred aircraft armed with TNT bombs. Moreover, these weapons could be used when aircraft were grounded because of weather or were denied for other reasons. The U.S. Army attached high priority to small nuclear weapons of the tactical or battlefield type, and dozens of tests at the Nevada Proving Grounds were made to develop small, lightweight warheads with blast power measured in the kilotons.

The atom was to be a universal deterrent. Super-bombs or strategic weapons would deter the outbreak of global war. Tactical A-bombs would keep the peace on the local front. The combination would restrain the Soviets from marching across Europe or from invading Formosa. The New Look, based upon nuclear weapons, would moreover allow the total defense budget to be pared down so that the national budget might be balanced.

Would the family of nuclear weapons keep the peace? To my mind the question involves discussion of two very important topics. First, the question as to whether nuclear weapons can be used in a local war without that conflict erupting into a bigger war. In other words, can a nuclear war be limited? Second, the problems raised by the development of the ballistic missile and its relation to the strategy of war.

It is the nature of atomic energy and its impact upon world affairs that I find myself writing about military strategy. This subject has interested me ever since I witnessed the dazzling light and bone-crushing blast of an atomic explosion. And as I have mentioned earlier, I interested myself in the military aspects of atomic energy by serving for a number of years in the Pentagon. Having read what the military men write about the military atom, I believe that I need not apologize too profusely before setting out on a brief excursion into this field. There are really no military experts in the nuclear field, for the weapon has been little more than baptized in war.

When Defense Department spokesmen assert, as they have repeatedly done, that nuclear war can be limited, I feel very strongly that they should be challenged. I find it very difficult to believe that one could employ nuclear weapons in the defense of a densely populated country such as Germany. Not only would the bomb's punch be hard to confine to the immediate battle area because of its long reach, but, in addition, the highest priority targets for A-attack would be air fields, tank depots, basing points, rail hubs and marshalling areas far from the front line but close to civilian concentrations. The U.S. Army's development of Jupiter, a fifteen-hundred-mile ballistic missile, documents my fear. Thus, confining the bomb to a local battlefield would be exceedingly difficult. The temptation would be to use more bombs and bigger ones to score a knockout blow. The greater the number and the higher the power of the bombs used, the more probable it would be that the local war would expand. Indeed, fear of defeat would impel a losing commander to more extreme violence. This would be especially true where the local area of conflict was being fed supplies from a distant source. I wonder if one would ever encounter two opposing commanders sophisticated enough to employ nuclear weapons in moderate doses so that one could realize a condition of stalemate on the battlefield.

I think Herblock, the eminent cartoonist, summed it up beautifully: "To our military and budget planners, baby A-bombs may be conventional weapons, but to most of the world these babies are little monsters that might usher in full-size atomic war."

Those who theorize that nuclear weapons can be limited in battle are, in essence, hoping for a return of the Age of Chivalry in war. At one time, long ago, military forces conducted themselves with propriety. They kept towns and villages off limits and even restricted their fighting to certain days of the week. The only circumstances where I think such conduct might still be approachable would be on the high seas. I believe that naval engagements could be fought with nuclear weapons without having the violence spill over into land areas. But once A-bombs are used in ground conflict, I think it is the beginning of the end.

I realize full well that this strikes at the very heart of our defense planning. If nuclear weapons cannot be limited in local wars, what substitute is there for local deterrence?

Here I suggest that local deterrents-in-kind be used to combat peripheral aggression. Opposing the aggressors with men and conventional weapons will be costly, but it need not be ruinous *if* our Defense Department will make some radical changes in its organization and in its philosophy of war. I believe that a small, highly mobile force-in-being could be created which could be rushed to oppose aggression in peripheral areas, provided that (a) this force be backed up by the latent mobilization capacity of our industry (b) it is understood that no World War II type conflict would take place so that mobilization would be limited (c) the force standardize and minimize its equipment, or "hardware" as the military call it, and (d) true unification of the Armed Services is achieved to reduce duplication expenses.

My fundamental assumption is that local wars would be fought with guns, tanks and ordinary weapons whereas a global war would be nuclear. Thus, the possession of great nuclear striking power in the possession of the U.S.S.R. and the U.S.A., would be the strategic umbrella under which the local war would be limited. Again, I emphasize that unless local wars are conducted in the old-fashioned way without resort to nuclear weapons, there is too much risk that they will explode into a full-blown nuclear holocaust.

What I urge is in direct contradiction to the New Look in defense, which more and more attempts to convert the nuclear family into a docile breed indistinguishable from old-fashioned weapons. Unfortunately, the yawning gap between nuclear and conventional weapons is too great to be bridged. The smallest A-bomb may seem a tiny infant compared with the jumbo-sized Super but it is our *enfant terrible*.

Our military forces, both nuclear and non-nuclear, must be constantly renewed in order to deter. Our labors are therefore those of Sisyphus, condemned to push a heavy rock to the top of a hill and forced to repeat this onerous task over and over. For only if our defenses are ever ready, and always coequal, will the Soviet be deterred. Peace through mutual terror "does not make for serenity"; its great value is that it provides a breathing spell for the quaking world to assess its instability. Time granted us by the mutuality of destructive forces is all-important and must not be lost. If we squander these months and years, as we did during the development of Super, then we fail to grasp the meaning of the true situation in the split world of today.

Time is our most valuable asset in the uneasy calm bestowed upon us by the incredible power of modern weapons. This calm may be that before the storm, if we think that weapons, themselves, insure the peace.

Our most urgent problem is the establishment of conditions which will induce the Soviets to accept a new world order. The rupture between the East and the West may seem irreparable, but we must proceed just as though the planet were being invaded by Martians, intent on wiping out both the U.S.A. and the U.S.S.R. The nuclear family is our common enemy, and some mutual means must be devised to quarantine the whole family, both the Supers and babies. The international control of nuclear energy thus becomes our paramount problem.

Franklin D. Roosevelt never lived to witness the birth of atomic energy, but he was given a preview of its consequences by the great Danish physicist, Niels Bohr. The two met in Washington, D.C., a full year before Hiroshima, and the physicist briefed the President on the problem of international control of the yet-to-be unleashed elemental force:

Ever since the possibilities of releasing atomic energy on a vast scale came in sight, much thought has naturally been given to the question of control, but the further the exploration of the scientific problems concerned is proceeding, the clearer it becomes that no kind of customary measures will suffice for this purpose and especially the terrifying prospect of future competition between nations about a weapon of such formidable character can be avoided through universal agreement in true confidence.

The key word in this prevision of the Atomic Age is "confidence," for it is this quality above all others that must be sought between the split halves of the world. All too quickly the first decade of the postwar period slipped by, and all too precipitously the nuclear hazards accumulated. Today the problems are vastly different from those assumed by the UN's first approach to international control. The British and the Soviets both have the bomb and are accumulating formidable stockpiles. Bombs have grown so cheap, so easy to convert and so huge in power that any control plan advanced today must inevitably be quite different from those proposed when only the U.S. had custodianship of the weapon. The arms juggernaut is careening along on such a hazardous path that even Premier Bulganin warned: "It is clear that the arms drive, including that in the field of atomic weapons, is not diminishing but, on the contrary, is increasing the threat of a new war." Apparently, indeed evidently, the supreme penalties imposed by the superweapons are, in themselves, no real holdfast against the outbreak of war.

So, at last, man must turn aside from his centuries-old reliance upon armed might as his insurance against conflict. Man still lives on the same planet but it is now *terra infirma*. The world today is so different from the preatomic planet that it is almost as though man were reborn on another spinning planet. But the planet seems the same, the trees look as green and the lakes and oceans seem no different, so men persist in thinking as they did in the past. Our statesmen only gradually perceive the dim outlines of the new world, our generals stick to the tradition of planning for the last war but add a touch of hideous novelty, and the world's populations slumber on.

Man is engaged in a reckless gamble which is epitomized in government circles along the lines:

"There will be no war because the weapons are now too terrible." The selfsame men who mouth this superficiality impose rigid secrecy upon the nature of these weapons, and thus do not even see the relation between advertisement of the terror and their smug policies. But, basically, the fallacy of their reasoning is that they think along purely military lines. We have already insisted that our national defenses must be readied and adequate, but we have emphasized that this merely provides time. Now we ask: time for what?

The answer is obviously not time for more military preparation. We must seek solution in non-military avenues, even though we see no well-defined highway to travel. The ultimate solution is international control based upon mutual trust and mutual inspection of each other's facilities. Unilateral action, say, in disarmament would be equivalent to letting down our guard before an unreasoning pugilist. Our negotiations in the area of control of the new weapons must proceed from a solid base of armed strength. Failure to operate from a position of strength would, in my view, invite destruction. Sir Winston Churchill emphasized: "Of one thing I am quite sure that if the United States were to consent in reliance upon any paper agreement, to destroy the stacks of atomic bombs which they have accumulated, they would be guilty of murdering human freedom and committing suicide, themselves."

Transition from the present-day standards of distrust, secrecy and hostility to openness, trust and friendship will not take place overnight. Rather it will come as a gradual gaining of confidence between nations with agreement on small things. Such small

beginnings are the vital prerequisites for mutual understanding on the great issues of disarmament. Where
do we begin? On what things can the Soviet and
non-Soviet worlds agree without imposing too great
a strain upon each other's faith?

Obviously, we cannot expect that the Soviets will
throw open the doors of their bomb vaults or open
the gates of their missile ranges. This would be too
much to expect either from them or from us. Of the
various plans which have been proposed for nibbling
away at the inspection problem those which do not
violate national sovereignty appear to be most attractive and hopeful of success. We must therefore ask
ourselves what it is possible to inspect without sending
an army of inspectors inside a nation's borders.

Here the scientists come to the rescue for they have
devised the technical means for "snooping" without
using either the cloak-and-dagger route or formal
penetration of the Iron Curtain. We refer to the
instrumental techniques of monitoring nuclear detonations from remote locations. These long-range detection
systems, which we have described, are quite foolproof
and can be relied upon to detect an atomic explosion
anywhere on the globe. A proposal advanced by some
U.S. scientists called for the United Nations to negotiate a truce on nuclear tests which would be "enforce-
able" through a network of UN-manned detection
posts. Ceasing the tests, it was argued, would curtail
progress not only in the nuclear field but would affect
the allied development of ballistic missiles in that a
suitable warhead might, itself, be delayed. The idea
was to have *all* nations agree to the test ban. Should

a nation test weapons, in violation of the agreement, the offender would be discovered by the UN detection net and hence would be brought before an adverse world opinion—a court to which even the Soviets are sensitive.

The proposal to cease nuclear tests had a number of obvious advantages. First and foremost, it is a practicable scheme which does not require ripping apart any Iron Curtains for an international inspectorate. Second, it is a first step which might foster the atmosphere of co-operation and trust essential to more drastic agreements. Thirdly, it is one of the last stopping points before the brink of the chasm—the development of the long-range ballistic missile.

One real drawback to the plan is that it singles out superweapons in the test ban. Where would one draw the line between strategic and tactical weapons? If one drew a line, say, at bombs above a hundred kilotons in power, how could one be sure of policing this limit? A nation might be accused of exceeding the limit only to alibi, "We achieved greater success than we planned." Furthermore, nations would be anxious to apply the compound fission principle of the super-bomb to smaller and smaller weapons in order to make these more cheaply. For these reasons I believe that it is wise to apply the test ban to all nuclear weapons regardless of size.

So far the Soviet Union has been the one to plead for test bans whereas the United States has summarily rejected such proposals. By so doing, the U.S.A. has given a distinct propaganda edge to the Soviets who thus appear to the world as the nation favoring abolition of these weapons. Three nations already possess these special explosives, and a fourth, then a fifth, and a sixth will join the nuclear ranks. It is to our advantage to prevent the fourth power from becoming a nuclear-equipped nation, for a multiplicity of world atomic powers is a fear-filled, egg-on-end dilemma. Cessation of nuclear tests would undeniably limit the number of nuclearly-armed powers and, in addition, might put some brakes on technical progress which so swiftly outruns man's political-international advances.

President Eisenhower has commented on the test cessation by stating that (a) a test ban would limit progress in the development of defensive nuclear weapons such as anti-aircraft devices and (b) it is paradoxical to restrict development of an explosive while increasing effort on the missile designed to carry the warhead. The first point is certainly a valid one, but is just part of the concession that had to be made in the interest of slowing down the out-of-control arms race. However, the second brings up a further step which we might take seriously. Experts all agree that the day of the intercontinental ballistic missile is not far off; they disagree only on the development date and on the reliability of the weapon. Why not consider a test ban which would include not only nuclear weapons but also long-range ballistic missiles? The art of detecting missiles in flight is less advanced than the long-range detection of nuclear tests, but it is less conceivable that missiles could be monitored without invading sovereign territory. A few UN-operated radar posts strategically located inside each continent might be considered.

The day of the nuclear-armed ballistic missile capable of spanning thousands of miles will usher in ultimate weaponry and hair-trigger coexistence. Take-off to target times of twenty to thirty minutes give some concept of the abridgment of the time dimension of missile warfare. Such time scales will make "massive instant retaliation" a reflex mechanism devoid of human decision, for there will not be time for cabinet meetings or Congressional consultations with the White House. One attack will trigger the other, and the predictions of H. G. Wells will then become a reality. Clearly, peace through mutual terror in the era of ballistic missiles will be a jittery proposition.

This grim prospect is what is in store unless men come to an agreement to control this new force. The world will have reached the "stage in this story where safety will be the sturdy child of terror and survival the twin brother of annihilation," to use Sir Winston Churchill's language. The greatest British leader of our time had searched his soul, and yet he found no more comforting security than a restatement of his "peace through mutual terror."

The alternative is easily phrased—lasting peace based upon controlled disarmament—but nations have a long way to go and many sacrifices to make before this formula can be adopted. National self-interest must be made subordinate to world order. Sovereign power must be secondary to a global system of disarmament and a unified supranational police force.

Attainment of the ultimate goal of a global authority transcending the power of any one nation will be infinitely difficult. However, the difficulty will increase as time elapses and thrusts us more and more into the terror-laden arsenal of modern weaponry. We must arm, and maintain our arms; but at the same time we must pursue the paths of peace toward international disarmament. This will be more difficult in the future if the Soviets cut back on conventional armed forces and, themselves, adopt a New Look which focuses on the atom. Traditionally, the Soviets have sought security in geography (buffer satellites); they may now look upon nuclear weapons as their best defense.

However, it should not be imposible to imagine situations which might make disarmament more attractive to the Soviets than continuing a resource-destroying military economy which imposes immense burdens on the backs of the Soviet people. Significant, and indeed remarkable, changes have occurred in Soviet life in the past few years since the death of Stalin. It is not unreasonable to expect that even more significant changes are possible. The Soviet leaders must certainly know the consequences of a nuclear war, and we may rightfully place some hope in the awesome power of the nuclear arsenal. "The Good News of Damnation" may, indeed, not be far of the mark.

Nuclear weapons cannot be used without limit in war for the radioactive fall-out imposes or should impose restrictions. They cannot be put in the same category as a TNT shell or bomb. Yet when Lt. Gen. James M. Gavin testified on strategic bombardment before a Senate group on May 22, 1956, he stated: "Current planning estimates run on the order of several hundred million deaths—that would be either way depending upon which way the wind blew." Apparently U.S. military planning looks upon the nuclear weapon as "just another weapon" in its arsenal—a weapon to be used at will.

Superbombs have shrunk the dimensions of our planet and should, if men everywhere understand their meaning, become the dictators of peace. But a basic precondition for such a peace is universal comprehension of the full potency of the atom. If such knowledge does not deter war, then we can only conclude that man is a witless creature.

chapter 10

ATOMS FOR PEACE

Dr. J. Robert Oppenheimer took a new look at his scorpions in a bottle after he "retired" from his advisory role with the U.S. government. Viewing the situation from the "outside" in 1956, the former Los Alamos chief made a new assessment. "We have a world full of new states and wounded national fervor," Oppenheimer began, and continued: "We have a situation now where super powers have super weapons that they mustn't use. We have a world in which unless something is done about it, all states will be armed to the teeth with this stuff within a couple of decades."

This frightening world of Dr. Oppenheimer's is a jugful of scorpions. Such an abundance of stinging creatures represents—to use his words—"a very brittle kind of stability." Two wise scorpions might respect each other's lethal power (although biology refutes this), but a crowd of scorpions is a most unwholesome company. This is, in fact, the very situation we forewarned of in urging the cessation of tests in the last chapter, namely, the fourth-power dilemma.

President Eisenhower, in the very speech which dealt with atomic colossi, urged a new approach to bridge the deepening rift between the world community. Speaking before the United Nations on December 8, 1953, the President spoke out: "I know that in a world divided, such as ours today, salvation cannot be attained by one dramatic act. I know that many steps will have to be taken over many months before the world can look at itself one day and truly realize that a new climate of mutually peaceful confidance is abroad in the world." America's most honored general then spoke of a "new avenue of peace" which should be explored—international co-operation in the peaceful uses of atomic energy. Eisenhower proposed that "if the fearful trend of atomic military build-up can be reversed, this greatest of destructive forces can be developed into a great boon, for the benefit of all mankind."

This was the President's "atoms for peace" plan which excited so much enthusiasm on the part of the majority of the United Nations. An Atomic Energy Agency would be established to act as custodian for the fissionable material necessary for the production of atomic power. The same uranium material useful in a bomb can be used in a reactor for the production of electrical power. This material would be pooled by the various "have" nations and shared with the "have-nots."

The basic purpose of the President's atomic pool proposal is to provide power-starved areas of the world with electrical energy from atomic plants. A direct dividend of this plan would be the fostering of mutual confidence between nations. Another dividend would be a manifestation that atomic energy need not be destructive but could be man's obedient servant. Additionally, the President felt that it would "begin to diminish the potential destructive power of the world's atomic stockpiles," apparently by diverting material from bomb use to power production. "Atoms for peace" might, it was felt, be the antidote for the military atom.

No advance warning or even an inkling had been given that President Eisenhower would make such a dramatic gesture as his atoms-for-peace proposal on December 8, 1953. Indeed, there is good evidence that only a very few cabinet-level officials knew of the plan. Even the Atomic Energy Commissioners (excepting the chairman, Admiral Strauss) confessed later that they had no advance knowledge that such a plan was under consideration. Probably not even those in the know had any real appreciation of the excitement which the President's proposal would evoke among nations such as India, Japan, Italy, the Latin American countries and others. Had they gauged the reaction, they would undoubtedly have had specific proposals on hand to implement the President's bold approach. It was a case of the "Injuns" not knowing what the "Chiefs" were up to, and consequently no one at a lower level in the AEC was prepared with the spade-work details for the plan.

Fortunately, the proposal caught the Soviets off guard, too, and the hiatus which followed December 8 was not too embarrassing to the U.S.A., for the Soviets took quite a few months to recover from the precipitant proposal.

President Eisenhower's atomic plan raises some very serious questions along the following lines:

Is nuclear power technically capable of aiding foreign nations?

Can adequate safeguards be devised to keep account of

nuclear fuel and prevent an atomic power plant from becoming a bomb producer?

Is the United States prepared to implement its plan by sharing technical know-how with other nations?

Will the demand of power plants for nuclear fuel be great enough in the near future to siphon off bomb material from military uses?

What is the danger that we will accelerate the nuclear arms race (the fourth-power problem) by aiding other nations in nuclear technology?

These questions are complex ones which we cannot answer abruptly, and, even after paving the way for answers in the next chapters, it is clear that only future developments will provide real answers.

The irony of nuclear power is that the material it uses, and that which it can produce, is potentially bomb stuff. Furthermore, it is relatively easy to convert this material into a bomb, whereas the art of producing nuclear power in a plant that must operate for several decades in order to be of commercial utility is a difficult undertaking. A-bombs and superbombs are a reality today, whereas practical or economic nuclear power for peaceful uses is still in the future.

For a full year following the hatching of the atoms-for-peace plan there was little forward movement among the nations approving of the plan. The year 1955 saw a quickened tempo in developments with the U.S.A. signing bilateral agreements with two dozen nations for limited co-operation on small-scale or research reactors. The U.S. Atomic Energy Act of 1946 had been revised to permit more extensive co-operation with other countries, but the 1954 revision of the Act still hemmed in the field of nuclear power with secrecy and security restrictions which inhibited the development of atomic energy both at home and abroad.

The big stimulus which international atomic energy received in 1955 came from the Geneva Conference on Peaceful Uses of Atomic Energy which convened on August 8. Representatives of seventy-three nations met in the ornate Palais des Nations. Over one thousand scientific and technical papers were prepared for the conference, and the world waited for this first historic meeting of atomic scientists from Russia, U.S.A., Britain and many other nations to take place. Naturally, many onlookers were jittery that the Soviets might try to use the floor of the Palais as a stage for a propaganda coup. However, ground rules were hammered out well in advance which were strictly adhered to by all concerned. Admiral Lewis L. Strauss headed up the U.S delegation and became known as "the father of the conference"—a parentage which he welcomed, once it became apparent that the conference was going to be a big success. It was rather a strange role for the Admiral, who only six years before had been so passionately opposed to sharing even a few radioisotopes with foreign countries that his fellow commissioners dared scarcely even mention the word "isotope" to him, lest it precipitate an agonizing debate.

The U.S. delegation included many topnotch scientists plus the usual entourage of visiting firemen. Over all, the Atomic Energy Commission gave an excellent account of itself, both in the quality of the papers read at the meetings and in the exhibits on display in Geneva. It was, as it turned out, not a purely scientific conference after all, but rather a political-technical meeting to which all U.S. scientists went as delegates "cleared" by the AEC. Thus, such outstanding physicists as Robert Oppenheimer and Edward Condon, to name a few, were barred. One European scientist said to me, "Had Oppenheimer come to Geneva, it would have been a great success for you."

I remember very well the feeling which many of us had when the Geneva conference opened. We were, quite naturally, interested primarily in what the Soviet scientists would have to say, in how freely they would talk and in the extent to which they might loosen up in private conversation. It must be remembered that the Iron-Uranium curtain between the U.S.S.R. and U.S.A. had never been previously punctured; almost everything we knew about Soviet nuclear progress came from indirect sources, such as the errant winds which wafted telltale atoms around the world to reveal the nature of Soviet tests. Such topics would be out of bounds for our initial discussions; we had to stick to uranium fission and atomic power. The quality of the Soviet contributions to the conference proceedings was high, and, in general, the Russian representatives knew what they were talking about and seemed quite proud of their achievements. They talked quite freely, accepted luncheon and dinner invitations and gave little evidence of being ill at ease.

The difficult customers to deal with were the Soviet press aides who holed up in a Geneva hotel and proceeded to give every correspondent the run-around.

Yes, they would be delighted to answer questions; submit them in writing and come back Tuesday. On Tuesday, there would be a new man in charge and again the routine, write out your questions . . . with the result that no answers were forthcoming.

A number of us looked for signs that Soviet progress in the nuclear field might derive from imported German talent. This did not seem to be the case, and later we found out that those German experts who did go to Russia remained isolated from the Russian experts and did not get in on important developments. Some of the Soviet delegates were well known to us from their prewar work, but many were quite new and it was difficult for us to determine whether the Soviets had sent their first or second team to Geneva. As one colleague remarked to me, "If these men are on the second team, I sure would like to see the first team." In summary, then, the Soviets made first-rate contributions at Geneva.

Perhaps the greatest contribution which the Soviets made was the breaking out into the open of data held secret in the United States for over a decade. One of the reasons for withholding information or refusing to "declassify" nuclear data has always been that it could not be *proved* that the Soviets knew the facts. So once the Soviets published the data, we were smoked out and had to release much information from the secret category.

My own impression was that the most significant U.S. contribution at Geneva was the construction of a working reactor right on the grounds of the Palais. Thousands of Europeans filed through the exhibit and were able to peer down through clear water and see the core of an atomic reactor. Seeing is believing, and the swimming-pool type reactor we demonstrated at Geneva took much of the mystery away from atomic energy.

On the other side of the fence, the U.S. received from other nations at the Conference a feeling for the need which these countries have for a new power source. Indian representatives confessed rather pathetically that, in their country of four hundred million people, three-fourths of the energy used comes from the burning of dried cattle dung. Imagine a land perpetually on the rim of famine, burning up the very material needed for their crop land. Other nations, such as Switzerland and Japan, were much higher on the rungs of the industrial ladder, but yet they admitted to an urgent need for a substitute for coal or hydro-power. Britain, which had ushered in the Age of Steam Power, put high priority on uranium power, for it found it increasingly difficult to exploit thinning and deepening seams of coal. Carrying coal to Newcastle reversed in meaning as the British looked to their fuel lockers and found them wanting.

Among the many nations of the world, Britain and the Soviet Union contended with the U.S.A. in the race for nuclear power. The British, led by the shrewd Sir John Cockcroft, revealed an ambitious nuclear power program at Geneva. The first British atomic power installation, placed in operation late in 1956, is the Calder Hall plant near the northwest coast. Rated at over fifty thousand kilowatts of electrical generating capacity, the Calder Hall plant is the first in the Free World to provide practical power from uranium. The British are bullish about the atom and are striding ahead toward a goal of eighteen reactors to be built during the next decade. They hope to supply close to two million kilowatts of nuclear-electric power by 1965, and ten years after that they plan for one-fourth of all their electrical power to be of nuclear origin.

The Soviets seem equally optimistic about the prospects for atomic power. They have revealed in their last (the sixth) Five Year Plan that over two million kilowatts of electrical power will come from atom-splitting. Reporting to the twentieth Congress of the Communist party meeting in Moscow, leading atomic expert, Ivan V. Kurchatov stated: "Two atomic electric stations with a total capacity of 1 million kw will be built in the Urals by 1960 and near Moscow there will also be built an atomic station with a capacity of 400,000 kw." Kurchatov added that the Soviet Union would build "up to ten types of atomic reactors with individual electric capacities from 50 to 200 thousand kw." Apparently, the first practical large-scale nuclear power reactor in the Soviet Union will go into operation in 1958, although this starting date is still uncertain.

Here at home, the nuclear power picture has been somewhat confused and uncertain. Our first nuclear electric plant at Shippingport, Pennsylvania, in the heart of cheap coal area, will swing into operation in 1957 and is slated to produce an initial sixty thousand kilowatts of power, with a maximum of a hundred thousand when it is perfected. Our next five-year period for reactor construction will see a maximum of about eight hundred thousand kilowatts of electrical power or roughly a third of the Soviet goal.

These comparative figures tempt one to jump to the conclusion that the United States is trailing in the A-power contest. Certainly, there is little doubt that we are engaged in a technological competition with the other nations of the world. But it is too early to judge the one, two, three order of the contestants. My own view is that the British have frozen their reactor plans too early, because of an urgent domestic requirement for power and that the Soviets do not have as broad a base for their reactor development as we do. In other words, I believe that the total number of A-plants or the total kilowatts installed by a given date do not necessarily determine the running order of each country.

I do not want to stand as an apologist for the present nuclear power program of the Atomic Energy Commission, for I have criticized it frequently as being too timid and too unimaginative in approach. But I do believe that a number of factors tend to explain why the United States does not have a more vigorous nuclear-electric power program.

First, we live in a nation which has been blessed with great reserves of natural resources, especially in such fossil fuels as coal, natural gas and petroleum. Our beds of coal are so rich that they hold fuel for centuries. Our reserves of premium fuels, gas and oil, are less abundant but are not in short supply for the immediate future. Therefore, we have had less motivation for the development of domestic atomic power.

Second, we have been preoccupied with military

development in the field of atomic energy to the extent that roughly nine-tenths of our effort has gone into weaponry and bomb material production. In this blind obedience to the dictates of the Pentagon, I believe that the Atomic Energy Commission has been myopic. The AEC did not see the importance of peacetime A-power either as a matter of national prestige or as a powerful instrument for aid to our Allies.

Third, we have been so obsessed with secrecy that we have ham-strung our own progress in peacetime atomic development. This stultifying secrecy coupled with a monopolistic AEC policy has intimidated U.S. industry. Even when the original McMahon Act was revised in 1954 to provide more incentives and get U.S. industrialists into the act, the response was not too enthusiastic. In part, we come back to our first point, namely, to the abundance of cheap power already available in the U.S.A. American businessmen are not going to risk capital on a power source which does not promise to provide a cheaper source of kilowatts than coal or hydropower. Moreover, nuclear reactors are expensive single packages which promise more efficient power in very high-power units which may cost more than fifty million dollars apiece.

However, I believe that President Eisenhower's atoms-for-peace proposals jarred the AEC loose from its conservative policies on atomic power. If we are to live up to the terms of the President's expressed objectives, we must become the leaders in the art of nuclear power. Accordingly, more and more research is being put on this new development, and I think that the work is being conducted on a broad enough base so that it gives promise of ultimately providing superior nuclear installations.

President Eisenhower was reported to be irked at the lack of follow-through for his original proposals and again took the initiative early in 1956, when he offered to make forty-four tons of fissionable material available for nuclear industry. Half of this atomic pool would be set aside for home industry and half would be earmarked for the international market. Although dollar values are not too well pegged for this nuclear fuel, the President's offer involves close to a billion dollars in material.

At the present time, this offer is somewhat like the grapes over the head of Tantalus. The material is within reach, but, to make it truly useful, the foreign nations need information and know-how. The U.S. is still so transfixed by its secrecy specter that it is unwilling to go all the way. Even at home industrialists must receive special security clearance, called L-access, in order to receive atomic power data. This L-access is, in my estimate, a thinly disguised fraud, for it still keeps out of reach all secret data, allowing the industrialist to see only confidential information. We should know now that we are dealing with a mature and competent competitor in the Soviet Union, and that our policy on atomic secrecy is that of an ostrich burying its head in sand, refusing to see what should be obvious.

About two years ago I was revising a book on nuclear physics, and I wanted to include in it a graph showing the behavior of the uranium atom with respect to neutrons of various speed. I knew that the data were still held secret, but I did wish to illustrate the approximate nature of the uranium atom's behavior by drawing a straight line in place of the very jagged, wiggly curve stamped "Secret" in AEC files. All I needed was one point on the curve to serve as an anchor point; this was stricken out by the AEC blue-pencil experts. I could not help remembering this censorship when I received a Soviet scientific paper at Geneva and discovered that the complete curve was in it. It was the *same* as ours. One might jump to the conclusion that it had been stolen, but the Soviets presented loads of data showing how they made their measurements independently. It was most encouraging to note that nuclear physics obeys the same laws on each side of the Iron Curtain, but, personally, I was upset that a nation as dynamic as the United States should blindfold itself with an obscuring mask of secrecy. Nuclear power development is tough enough, technically, without giving our engineers books with pages missing.

The atoms-for-peace conference at Geneva convinced our first-rate scientists that we are now engaged in a long-term competition, not only in the area of nuclear science, but in the larger realm of science as well. Soviet scientists are being produced in ever increasing numbers. On the authority of Mr. Allen Dulles, director of the Central Intelligence Agency, I can spout the following statistics: during 1955 Soviet advanced schools graduated about eighty thousand men and women in the physical sciences (with a high proportion of women as compared with U.S.A.), whereas in the United States the corresponding figure was thirty-seven thousand graduates. In other words, the U.S.S.R. more than doubled the U.S. production of physical scientists. The payoff for this stepped-up Soviet program in science will come within a decade or two, but the challenge is with us now. And this challenge is quite apart from the fact that we have a foreign competitor (I get somewhat weary of having the U.S. take action because of something the Soviets do); our normal domestic demand for scientists far exceeds the supply.

Almost any scientist or engineer earning his diploma today is snowed under with offers from industry and government. He can take his pick, for industry needs three times more men than are available. One might think that in the long run the laws of supply and demand would rectify this situation of scarcity. But in this case the law of supply has to work its way all down the line from college to high school and even down to grade school. Science teachers in high school are urgently needed, yet the good ones are constantly pirated by industry and government, itself, so that the situation is made worse. Moreover, the youth of America must be stimulated to want to become scientists. This will not be easy for physics, mathematics and chemistry are not snap courses; yet they are the mandatory steppingstones for future scientists.

In the long run American supremacy in the field of nuclear energy will depend upon its future brain power. I firmly believe that individual brain power will be more important than the total number of brains which each country can muster. By that, I mean that the spark of genius is more significant than the slow heat of a thousand technicians. There are many surprises awaiting us tomorrow, and the men who tap these first and exploit them most quickly will be the bulwark of their country's security. We need more Fermis and Rutherfords, more Einsteins, more men of true genius to light the way to the future. Not only do we need these men but we also need to provide a nourishing climate for them so that their ideas will bear full fruit.

Genius is such a fragile quality that we must never again stand by and witness the revolting spectacle of the anti-science movement which fastened its ugly hold upon the United States during Senator McCarthy's heyday. Looking back, one shudders at the book-burning, the ridicule of professors, the denial of passports, the refusal of visas, the cancellations of research contracts and the other attacks upon science. These are largely past, but they can recur for we have no natural immunity to such malignancy.

We must provide a free and open atmosphere for high-quality research in the United States. And it is our responsibility to co-operate with the scientists of other nations in what Professor Einstein called the "international community." Scientists speak the same language and have the same ultimate objective—the pursuit of truth—so that they are most able to co-operate on an international basis. A useful supplement to President Eisenhower's atomic pool plan might be the establishment of a system of international laboratories under UN sponsorship, open to scientists of all nations. If the scientists, representing a segment of a nation's people, work shoulder to shoulder in mutual harmony, then it will be a step toward the ultimate goal of world peace.

President Eisenhower pledged the support of the United States, that day on December 8, 1953, when he stood before the assembled United Nations in its magnificent setting in New York City, "to help solve the fearful atomic dilemma—to devote its entire heart and mind to find the way by which the miraculous inventiveness of man shall not be dedicated to his death, but consecrated to his life."

chapter 11

NUCLEAR MACHINES

The World's Fair, to be held in Brussels in 1958, will feature a nuclear machine that will provide power and light for the spectacular exposition. Westinghouse Electric has contracted to build the special electrical plant which will be located near the environs of the Belgian capital.

When I first read of this announcement some impish cerebral connection stimulated me to dig back into my files. There I found what I sought—a faded dittoed press release dated April 13, 1946, from General Groves's office. The two-page release stated that the Manhattan Project had authorized the Monsanto Chemical Corporation to proceed with the design and construction of the world's first atomic power plant at Oak Ridge, Tennessee. According to General Groves, the plant would be ready to operate late in 1946 or early in 1947. He warned that it was an experimental pilot plant and that "a great amount of work remains to be done before fissionable material can be brought within the range of economic usability."

This first atomic *pile*, as it was called in the days before the present usage of *reactor*, was never built. Dr. Farrington Daniels, the designer of the first power pile, tackled the task with all of his boyish enthusiasm and adult experience, but the scheme folded up as the newly created Atomic Energy Commission inherited the assets of the Manhattan Project. Quite evidently, the Commission did not regard the Daniels pile as an asset. Being a very close friend of Dr. Daniels and also being close to things in Washington, I used to tell him that his plant was as dead as a dodo. Daniels, who is now chairman of the Department of Chemistry at the University of Wisconsin, is one of the highest principled men I have ever met. And he is also blessed (or cursed, depending on your point of view) with keen vision for the future. "Ralph," I recall his words as we argued on a Constitution Avenue bench, "it's just as important to build this pile as it is to build bombs." I agreed with my chemist friend but I pointed out that the AEC was ruled by conservatives and advised by physicists. The Commissioners were afraid of making any mistakes or risky ventures, and the physicist advisors counseled for perfectionism. This combination, plus the top-heavy concentration of AEC military work, killed the Daniels pile.

From 1947 to 1956 is a long span of years in the Cold War, and I have often felt that, had Daniels built his pile, we would have greatly accelerated our nuclear progress to the point that President Eisenhower would not have had to talk of atomic power in the future for his atoms-for-peace plan. The Daniels atomic plant would have been a "quick and dirty" scheme designed to gain experience in pile design, to learn from doing and to give a stimulus to American industry by example. Daniels never looked upon his proposal as a long-term proposition, and I think he would have been pleased had the plant operated for only a year. The AEC badly needed practical experience in the new reactor art. Its turtle-like reactor progress so irritated the deferential Eugene P. Wigner, a noted reactor specialist, that he finally blurted out at an Oak Ridge meeting, "What the AEC needs to do most is to build a reactor that won't work!" This statement made early in 1948, a year after the AEC was in business, pinpointed the stagnation in the nuclear power field.

When the Atomic Energy Commission finally got around to formulating a reactor program, it decided to let the U.S. Navy carry the ball. In my opinion, it was Captain (now Admiral) Hyman G. Rickover, a hard-bitten human dynamo, who really hammered out the AEC's program. "Rick" was then and is today a most controversial character. Small, wiry and possessed of birdlike features, Rickover has the subtlety of a pile driver, and it seemed to me that he would rather use a pile driver when a tack hammer might do the job. The U.S. Navy could not agree on its use for nuclear power but it could agree on one fact—it had no use for Rickover. The admirals had no love for the man but this did not faze Rick, who had pinned his future on the atom. He drove himself and a small group of trainees almost to the breaking point in his intense campaign to put the Navy in the nuclear power business.

Rickover never had the slightest doubt about his objective; it was to build a nuclear Navy. Nowadays, the Navy seems to be headed in this direction, but after World War II most of the top brass felt that Rick was a collision-course radical. Nonetheless, the stubborn little captain kept plugging away, putting his lieutenants in key spots in naval circles, until late in 1947 the Joint Chiefs of Staff concurred that nuclear submarines might rate a priority. No overwhelming priority was assigned to the requirement, but any military priority commanded respect in the meek civilian atomic agency. Rather than press Congress for funds to develop civilian power reactors, the AEC went along with Rickover and adopted the philosophy: "Let the Navy foot the bill." This philosophy was not indecent, for civilian requirements have often been met through military prototypes, as in the case of aircraft, jet engines and lightweight diesels. However, I believe that civilian A-power was worth developing on its own without the expedient of having it limp in on a military crutch.

This is all water over the dam now, but as events turned out the AEC's leaning on the Navy for reactor prototypes did not produce the reactor designs which greatly advanced the civilian art. In fact, when industry finally got into the business of designing nuclear machines, it had to start almost from scratch. True, the millions of dollars invested in the nuclear propulsion program did produce some benefits in nuclear technology, but since these developments very often were cloaked in military-atomic secrecy, they were not too useful. One may argue that the existence of a body of military reactor data impedes international co-operation on a free basis and puts a drag on Eisenhower's atoms-for-peace plan.

The Navy's requirement for a nuclear engine to propel a submarine beneath the surface of the sea could be met because of an ideal characteristic of uranium fuel. That is, the uranium fuel produces heat without flame—it is oxygenless heat so that there is no requirement for air intake when the submarine is submerged. Chemical fuels must undergo combustion, whereas nuclear fuels derive their energy from the splitting of atoms. Nuclear fuels are exceedingly compact as compared with conventional fuels; a single pound of nuclear fuel is the energy equivalent of a quarter-million gallons of gasoline.

These are some of the advantages which convinced Rickover that uranium was the ideal fuel for the U.S.S. *Nautilus,* the world's first atomic submarine. But he also saw disadvantages. There was, of course, the over-all problem of developing a new power source previously untried. Could the reactor core be made rugged enough to stand the perils of the sea? Would core materials stand up over long periods of time? Could the machine be made foolproof so that it could be trusted for prolonged submerged voyages? Could the "deadly fumes," in this case the radioactive by-products of the chain reaction, be kept confined away from the crew? And could the machine be made small enough to fit inside the submarine's hull?

Many of these questions could not be answered when Rick headed up the Navy's propulsion project. Matters were made worse because what Rick was trying to do was to put the cart before the horse. Normally, the evolution of nuclear machines should have proceeded from massive large-based units to the more rugged, smaller propulsive devices. Rickover could not wait for the AEC's horse to be born, so he jumped directly to the Navy's cart. In the process Rick also jumped from captain to admiral, although he did it the hard way, having been twice passed by the Navy's Selection Board.

Rickover put plenty of old-fashioned steam behind the construction of the *Nautilus* so that its power plant was first started up in 1954, just barely getting under the wire for that year by operating on December 30. "Four days later," Rick bragged, "it was developing full power alongside the dock. Then on January 17, 1955, she put to sea, and within six days she had completed a grueling series of sustained high-speed test runs, which included more than 50 dives." He also stated that the new nuclear-powered underseas craft "steamed" totally submerged from New London, Connecticut, to San Juan, Puerto Rico, a distance of about thirteen hundred miles in eighty-four hours. This was ten times farther than any submarine had ever traveled totally submerged, and the average speed of sixteen knots was record-breaking.

The *Nautilus* is powered by Mark II in a series of nuclear propulsion plants. Mark I is a land-based prototype which was built and tested at the AEC's reactor "farm" near Arco, Idaho. This first nuclear engine was built inside a simulated pressure hull and underwent its first testing in the spring of 1953. Thereafter, naval experts gained experience with it and ironed the bugs out of the version which Westinghouse Electric built to fit into the hull made by General Dynamics' Electric Boat Division at Groton, Connecticut. It was a tight squeeze, not because of the size of the reactor but rather because of the thick shield which enveloped the pressure vessel or reactor core. Inside the heart or core of the machine which drives the *Nautilus* is a nuclear reactor, which consists of highly enriched uranium fuel rods surrounded by a moderator of ordinary water. Coolant tubes made of zirconium traverse the reactor core, feeding in cool water and taking out water at high pressure and high temperature. The splitting atoms of uranium fuel produce the heat, which is then transferred to the coolant water which, in turn, is taken out of the pressure vessel to an external heat exchanger. The pressure vessel, itself, is a million-dollar item the construction of which taxed the facilities of boiler manufacturers. A huge cylinder of steel with a stainless-steel inner liner, it is topped with a hemispheric cap which is welded and bolted to the main vessel.

Once an engineer is given high-pressure, high-temperature water, he has power. All he has to do is to pass it through a boiler to produce steam in the boiler water and then harness the steam with a turbine. The nuclear reactor substitutes for the firebox of ordinary steam plants such as produce electricity in most American cities. In the case of the *Nautilus,* the steam produced turns a turbine which couples to the drive shaft. Steam fed into the turbogenerator can produce electricity sufficient for the needs of a community with twenty thousand people.

Pumps must be provided in the *Nautilus* to recirculate the coolant water in the closed-cycle system connected to the reactor and the boiler. Extreme care must be taken to make all parts as perfect as possible so that operational failures are minimized. This was a challenge to engineers since some of the materials specified for the *Nautilus* engine were most unusual. Take zirconium, for example. This shiny, silvery metal was an *objet d'art* prior to the development of reactors, yet it had to be produced by the ton to manufacture the internal parts for the *Nautilus* core. Ordinary construction materials do not qualify for reactor parts since they either corrode too quickly, will not stand the impact of nuclear radiation or will rob the chain reaction of valuable neutrons. The latter requirement strictly limits the number of metals which one can put inside a nuclear machine without stopping the chain reaction. Zirconium is excellent in its neutron characteristics, whereas steel, for example, would be very unsatisfactory due to its impurities.

The fuel rods are probably the most critical item in a nuclear reactor and they are constantly undergoing design and development. These rods must contain the nuclear fuel, of course, and they must stand up under the extreme temperature and havoc caused by the splitting of atoms. Consider a solid rod of uranium fuel; if you fission 10 per cent of the atoms (i.e., 10 per cent burn up), this means that one-tenth of the original uranium atoms leave their initial position in the rod. Such a mass transformation can produce crumbling or fissures in the rod. In addition, the fuel rod designer must make sure that his uranium fuel does not spit its split atoms into the circulating coolant, for this would contaminate the nuclear engine. This requirement is usually met by coating the rod with a jacket which will not corrode, crack or deform during its life in the machine.

We shall leave these technical details to the experts and proceed on the basis that future research and development will provide an adequate "black box" or nuclear reactor. But I do feel that one comment is needed. Nuclear energy is now in the hands of the engineers; the science of reactors is pretty well explored as compared with the engineering aspects of reactors. One cannot help but feel that the atom gets treated rather shabbily in a nuclear reactor, for its splitting provides potentially immense temperatures but these cannot be harnessed with our present-day technology. Thus, we "degrade" the atom's heat down to a mere few thousand degrees fahrenheit before we tap it; quite a comedown for the atom—it's like hooking a jet engine to a Civil War buggy. This limitation is imposed by our present state of metallurgy, but we can hope that new materials will be developed which will allow less of a horse-and-buggy approach to atomic power.

Even before the *Nautilus* was proved out as a seaworthy craft, the U.S. Navy had authorized a sister submarine powered by a different kind of reactor. The *Nautilus* is driven by a combination of uranium fuel plus ordinary water which reduces the neutrons to very low speed, so low that we call the neutrons "thermal," meaning that they are almost "dead" compared with their original high speed. Thus, the *Nautilus* is known as STR, standing for Submarine, Thermal Reactor. The second U.S. submarine incorporates an engine built by the General Electric Company—a stratagem of competition which Rickover felt might pit G.E. against Westinghouse in a race to perfect the best nuclear engine. The G.E. reactor is known as SIR, meaning Submarine, Intermediate Reactor, where the "intermediate" refers to the in-between speed of the neutrons which fission uranium. The neutrons are not allowed to slow down as much as in STR, and it was felt that this might make for a more compact, superior design. SIR powers the *Seawolf*, which put to sea in 1956, when the *Nautilus* had already broken many records for submarine performance.

Success with the *Nautilus* convinced both the Navy and Congress that nuclear propulsion made the diesel-electric submarines obsolete. Accordingly, six more nuclear-propelled subs were authorized to form the nucleus of a fleet of atomic submarines. Powered by SFR (Submarine, Fleet Reactors) machines, the first two of these underseas craft will cost about fifty-one million dollars' apiece, somewhat more than twice as much as a World War II sub. These two U-boats, the *Skate* and the *Swordfish*, are already under construction and work is progressing on SSN-585, the U.S.S. *Skipjack*, an attack submarine, smaller and faster than the *Nautilus*. Two more three-thousand-ton subs of the *Skate-Swordfish* class are planned, and, in addition, the Navy is designing a very large radar picket craft powered by twin reactors and costing $103 million.

Although the U.S. Navy was not very enthusiastic about nuclear propulsion at the beginning, it warmed up to this new power source once the *Nautilus* proved out. I suspect that the Navy's cool attitude toward nuclear propulsion was the result of (a) inertia in the slow-moving Bureau of Ships (b) reluctance to follow in Rickover's churning wake and (c) preoccupation with fighting the B-36 battle with the U.S. Air Force. Oddly enough, the latter point enters into the picture with the development of nuclear-powered craft.

The Navy-Air Force battle over the B-36 centered upon the delivery of nuclear weapons in strategic bombardment. The U.S. Air Force sought exclusive rights in the area of strategic delivery, while the air admirals fought bitterly to keep the Navy in on the act. While they were busy feuding, the nuclear-powered submarines were undergoing development and finally emerged as a real competitor to the long-range bomber. Nuclear submarines can cruise indefinitely below the surface, pop up suddenly and discharge intermediate-range missiles armed with nuclear warheads. The U.S. Navy has just such a missile submarine, nuclear-powered of course, under development. The advantages of this attack system are numerous: a dispersable and hard-to-hit base, and a close-in platform which obviates the use of intercontinental ballistic missiles, not to mention the fact that such platforms need not be located close to large metropolitan areas as is the case with some strategic air bases at home and abroad.

The Navy has under development reactors which may power large surface ships, such as its light cruiser for launching missiles. It has even more powerful nuclear machines in mind, capable of powering aircraft carriers, although this has been an on-again, off-again proposition in the Defense Department. Over all, nuclear power seems to be the shot in the arm which the Navy needed to keep it in business after it squandered much time and energy fighting the Air Force in a bitter interservice rivalry. If the Navy avoids the pitfall of being anchored to a fleet of supercarriers and pins its hopes on fast, light surface and subsurface vessels, it may well become the bulwark of our strategic deterrent policy.

Our Air Force also sees a link between the atom and a carrier for strategic nuclear weapons. No Johnny-come-lately, the Air Force seized upon the possibility of nuclear propulsion for aircraft shortly after the close of the war. Its NEPA (nuclear energy, propulsion, aircraft) project with the Fairchild Engine and Aircraft Corporation was its bid for a power plant running on uranium fuel. Once the Air Force realized that one pound of the new fuel was the equal of 1,700,000 pounds of gasoline, it decided that the A-plane would provide unlimited range—a characteristic which one cannot achieve in any bomber powered with a liquid petroleum product. The longer the range of a bomber and the higher its speed, the greater is the take-off weight of fuel that is required. In the huge B-36 bomber, for example, the fuel capacity amounts to a total of a hundred thousand pounds.

I had my first contact with the NEPA project when I attended a conference at Oak Ridge early in 1947 in my capacity as advisor to the War Department General Staff. We were given briefings on the aircraft project by a number of technicians and engineers, who displayed remarkable enthusiasm for their work and a lamentable knowledge of nuclear energy. It was quite apparent that some of the things they had in mind were absurd, as any qualified physicist could sense at a glance. For example, the wildest promises were made about the development of a lightweight shielding material—one of the sorest problems in harnessing nuclear power for aircraft—along the lines that if enough money were spent and energy expended a thin shield could be invented. The laws which neutrons and X rays obey in being absorbed are well known to scientists and have been understood for decades. In the case of the highly penetrating radiation emitted by split uranium atoms, for example, we know that it is sheer mass of material which stops the rays. Lead, gold or a similar dense material acts as a good absorber. For neutrons, the contrary is true, since light elements absorb best. Water is a good absorber for neutrons. Cutting down the radiation is thus a compromise proposition since both kinds of radiation have to be stopped. No wafer-thin material could do the job no matter how much money the Air Force spent; the laws of nature do not come within the command of the Defense Department.

The Air Force got off on the wrong foot in its NEPA project and finally the AEC, which had held itself aloof from the project, stepped in to evaluate the work. It was a real hot potato and the AEC juggled it only briefly and threw it into a special analytic project organized at the Massachusetts Institute of Technology in 1948. Dr. Walter Whitman became director of this Lexington Project which was to determine the feasibility of nuclear propulsion as a source of power for aircraft. The Whitman Report, which the AEC promised would be made public, never saw the light of day, but within the shade of government circles it produced stormy controversy. The Department of the Air Force interpreted the Whitman Report as meaning that nuclear-powered flight was feasible, whereas AEC experts viewed it differently. As they saw it, the development of aircraft nuclear engines had to await the orderly development of much more work on materials, shielding, heat transfer and a dozen other items. The argument simmered for many months, but meanwhile one effect of the MIT Lexington analysis was to focus research into the most critical areas and to make available to the Air Force much technical data and assistance from the AEC.

Things came to a head early in 1951 when it became evident that the NEPA project was not panning out very well. On February 22, the U.S. Air Force and the AEC made a joint announcement that the NEPA program would be terminated, marking the "completion of one phase of nuclear-powered flight program." Again, there was dispute over what this meant, the Air Force maintaining that work would be accelerated, whereas it was learned that the AEC interpreted this as meaning that the program was being reorganized on a new and longer time schedule.

To understand something of the problem which faced the AEC, one must realize that its facilities, and especially its scientific manpower, were already strained by existing research programs in weapons and bomb production. A great deal of effort was going into nuclear propulsion for submarines, and the AEC felt that it was overburdened with military chores. The Air Force, on the other hand, assigned a number two priority to its nuclear aircraft, placing it second only to the missile program.

The Air Force put on pressure for more emphasis on its A-plane engine, and the AEC knuckled under.

A huge program of intensified research was launched. The General Electric Company's Aircraft Gas Turbine Division set aside part of its Lockland, Ohio, plant for developing a nuclear power plant, and later the Pratt and Whitney Aircraft Corporation built a fifteen-million-dollar engine laboratory alongside the Connecticut River near Middleton, Connecticut. An atomic engine is less than half the job, for a specially designed airframe will be required to match the characteristics of the power plant. Much of this airframe work was assigned to the major aircraft companies, including General Dynamics' Convair plant at Fort Worth, Texas, Lockheed's Burbank, California, factory and Boeing's Seattle plant. Lockheed is building the nation's largest research and development facility for atom-powered aircraft near Dawsonville, Georgia.

Additional work on atomic aircraft is being conducted at the AEC's Oak Ridge installation, at the Wright Air Development Center in Dayton, Ohio, and at the facilities of the National Advisory Committee for Aeronautics' facilities. A test site has already been selected in Idaho where the AEC has a seventy-million-dollar test facility for the aircraft under construction, and is building a special runway more than three miles long for taxi tests of the new plane.

All in all, about three hundred million dollars have been spent on development of the new aircraft. Newspapers have featured headlines for a number of years, signaling the first take-off of a nuclear plane as being only one or two years in the future. The year 1958 has been widely advertised as the Kitty Hawk date for nuclear-powered flight, but I believe that this is too optimistic a forecast. Barring some spectacular advance in technology, I would guess that we will have to wait an additional five years for the aircraft to leave the ground under purely nuclear power. I suspect that when all the costs are counted, this first A-plane will represent a national investment of close to one-half billion dollars.

The important date from a military standpoint is not when the first A-plane takes off, but when we shall develop a militarily useful bomber. In the case of the Navy's submarine program, the first nuclear submarine turned out to have qualities which rendered it superior to old-fashioned underseas craft. But in the case of nuclear aircraft, the first A-plane is up against very serious competition. Unless it can exhibit high speed, its globe-circling range will not be sufficient to make it much more than a nuclear novelty. As Air Force Secretary Donald Quarles told a Congressional group: "Merely getting a nuclear aircraft into the air might be relatively simple. It would be very expensive and, under certain circumstances, wasteful. But if we can develop a nuclear-powered heavy bomber, we will have an extremely valuable weapon."

Nuclear engine designers can learn something from the Navy's experience with the *Nautilus* reactor, but they cannot borrow many pages from the Navy's book. The reasons are many: the Air Force needs a much lighter, yet more powerful reactor. Put another way, the ratio of reactor weight to propulsive power has to be a hundredfold different in order to get an A-bomber off the ground. Because more power is required, much more uranium has to be consumed per unit time. This, in turn, means that there will be a more intense source of penetrating radiation for which adequate shielding will be required.

Shielding the aircraft reactor is one of the toughest hurdles for the experts to surmount since the Air Force has set such minimum total weights for the complete A-power plant. Very probably the shield for the first A-plane will weigh in excess of fifty tons although some economy may be effected by cutting corners and by resorting to "shadow shielding." The latter is a trick technique designed to minimize the shield weight through the expedient of trimming off shield thickness in directions where the crew would not be found during flight. The biggest reduction in shield comes from paring down the size of the reactor core. The smaller the source of radiation, the smaller the total weight of shield; in fact, the trimming of a small amount of volume off the reactor core can involve a very big saving on shield weight. This can be easily appreciated if you compare the weight of a one-inch-thick covering for a billiard ball and a bowling ball.

Shrinking the size of the reactor core, however, necessarily increases the amount of heat produced per unit volume in the core; which means in turn that the core has to operate at a higher temperature and heat transfer from it must be greater. As in the nuclear submarine, the aircraft reactor core will produce heat which must be taken out in some useful form. The actual mechanism has not been revealed, but there are only a limited number of possibilities involved. In all probability, the method selected will involve the turbojet engine. The reactor's heat will substitute for the combustion of jet fuel in providing heat to the jet stream; but the reactor designers will have to work out a heat exchange system involving a fluid which re-circulates through the reactor. Incoming air will be heated up in this bulky heat exchanger, which, itself, may have to be surrounded with a shield. I suspect that this heat exchanger will be larger than the reactor itself, since it will have to transfer heat to air—a highly inefficient process. Some liquid metal like bismuth will have to be used as a coolant to pipe the heat out to the turbine-heat exchanger units buried in the fuselage of the bomber.

Nuclear bombers may after all be vehicles most useful to the Navy which could take them off from the sea's surface far from inhabited cities and land them with minimal risk of contaminating huge air bases. Atomic seaplanes are being actively pursued by the U.S. Navy. The U.S. Air Force has admitted that: "It is conceivable that a nuclear-powered, water-based air-craft may become an effective bomber suitable for the Air Force's wartime strategic bombing mission." The Air Force spokesman, General Thomas D. White also stated: "Used as a tanker, an aircraft which consumes none of the gasoline it carries and whose range is limit-less could permit intercontinental operation with every airplane capable of refueling in the air." One wonders if the Air Force view reflects a lack of confidence in the military worth of the nuclear bomber, consigning it to a tanker role rather than for strategic bombard-ment.

Unlimited range may be a great talking point for the nuclear aircraft, but from a military viewpoint there seem to be few missions for which such range is desirable. In view of the great weight of the nuclear power plant, the A-bomber may not be initially competitive with the chemically fueled jet bomber. Moreover, by the time the first nuclear aircraft is converted into a competitive bomber and is available in quantity, it will be up against even stiffer competition—the long-range ballistic missile. The competition enters on an even shorter time scale if one remembers that the Navy can take advantage of the more easily developed intermediate range ballistic missiles (IRBM).

This naturally raises the question: Can nuclear energy be adapted for missile propulsion? Missiles generally employ a propellant combination consisting of a fuel and an oxidant. The fuels include gasoline, alcohol or some hydrocarbon, and the oxidants range from liquid oxygen to nitric acid. These are housed in special tanks within the missile shell, and at the proper moment they are burned together in a combustion chamber. This combustion produces high temperature and pressure and forces the gaseous products through tubes, thus providing the essential thrust which propels the missile into the air. In empty space the rocket accelerates as more of the fuel-oxidant mixture is burned and hot gas is expelled into space. Expulsion of high-speed gas creates a reaction on the missile, according to Newton's well-known laws of action and reaction. The lighter the weight of the expelled gas (meaning in this case the molecular weight), the more efficient is the propulsive mechanism.

In the case of a nuclear missile, the role of the atom would be, as usual, a source of heat. The missile would have to be pushed forward by leaving something behind, so that in the nuclear propulsion system the missile would have to carry along some material to be heated and ejected backward. Liquid hydrogen would serve very effectively in this case. It would be heated up inside the nuclear reactor or in its heat exchanger and then be hurled outward, thrusting the missile forward.

Here again, we encounter the heat transfer problem so vexing in the instance of the nuclear aircraft engine. But in the case of a nuclear rocket, the problems would be much more severe since temperatures involved would be higher. However, the shielding problem would not be so severe since the rockets would not be manned. This does not mean that there would be no shielding requirement, for vacuum tubes and electronic devices used in the missile's internal controls would have to be shielded from direct reactor radiation. Long-range ballistic missiles are multiple stage, and it is conceivable that the last stage of a three-stage missile might incorporate a nuclear reactor in its propulsive system. Nuclear rockets, however, must be assigned a very long time scale in the indefinite future.

As man strides ever faster in his conquest of space and time, he uses greater and greater amounts of energy. One has only to compare the energy man uses in walking, or burns in driving a car, or consumes in an airplane or a rocket to appreciate the fantastic demands he makes upon fuel. It is thus inevitable that he should concentrate his attention upon nuclear substances which pound for pound are a millionfold richer in energy than chemical fuels.

A single pound of uranium fuel is enough to propel an aircraft completely around the world a number of times, the exact number depending upon what speed of travel and kind of plane you stipulate. The joker in this illustration is the fact that you need more than just a pound to make a reactor and you need the reactor. A gallon of gasoline can propel an automobile twenty miles along a highway if you drive sanely. But you need an internal-combustion engine under the hood to utilize the gasoline's energy, and in addition you need a transmission to relay the power from engine to driveshaft. It has taken automotive engineers over half a century to develop a relatively efficient, high-power gasoline engine. Given the same lapse of time, our nuclear engineers will perform wonders. If I am creaking around then, I think that I will find it an exciting world, vastly different from that of my childhood in the preatomic age.

chapter 12

THE ATOM'S POWER

One evening not long ago, I was relaxing after dining with some Washington friends, when they suggested tuning in a TV program on atomic energy. Before I had time to object, an AEC official was peering out of the screen, extolling the merits of atomic power. "Atomic energy will provide your children with electricity so cheap that it will not even be metered!" we were informed.

My friends, who pay monthly electric bills more or less regularly, were elated at this prospect, although their spirits were dampened somewhat that meterless power should be reserved for their children and not for themselves. I asked my host for his last electric bill and proceeded to calculate how much the total of $6.62 for that month would be reduced if uranium substituted for coal in the Potomac Electric Power Company's steam-electric plant. I made the rash assumption that the uranium fuel would cost PEPCO nothing instead of seven dollars per ton of coal for fuel. And I made the even rasher assumption that the company would pass on all this saving to the customers. Then I deduced that this free fuel would trim their monthly bill down to $5.47—a saving of $1.15. My friends were visibly disappointed, although perfectly willing to save a dollar.

The explanation for the meterless power of the TV personality and the calculated reduction in the electric bill is that residential rates for electrical power are determined by much more than the cost of the coal burned at the central station. In fact, in our example, the fuel cost amounts to roughly 17 per cent of the total cost. The other 83 per cent go to pay for the cost of the power plant, operations and maintenance, transformation and distribution of power and overhead.

If you are a manufacturer and use large quantities of electrical power, then your rates are much lower and eliminating fuel costs would make a much bigger difference to you. The percentage difference depends upon whether your plant is close to cheap coal or natural gas, or, in the case of TVA, you may be supplied with hydroelectric power. We shall not discuss the latter here for it constitutes a small fraction of U.S. electrical power, and this fraction will decline in the future as more and more of our energy derives from what we call the fossil fuels—coal, oil and natural gas.

Fuel costs are most expensive in the U.S.A. in four principal areas: northern New England, central Florida, most of Oregon and Nevada, and an area covering South Dakota extending up into North Dakota and Minnesota. Alaska has sky-high electricity because of the transportation costs for fuel. Alaskans can therefore be expected to be anxious to obtain a cheaper fuel, and it is not surprising that the Chugach Electrical Association has proposed a ten-thousand-kilowatt nuclear power plant for Anchorage, Alaska. The nuclear installation, itself, is very massive, but uranium as a fuel is essentially weightless compared with coal or petroleum—hence transportation costs are slashed sharply.

The Alaskan A-plant is rather a small one compared with the huge units being developed for producing electricity in the United States. The first full-scale nuclear-electric plant in the U.S.A. has been built on the banks of the Ohio River about twenty-five miles northwest of Pittsburgh. This Shippingport plant is located in a thinly populated area in which there is only one major industrial plant today. Viewed from the air, the first U.S.A.-plant is unusual in that it is not dominated by tall smokestacks so common to the Pennsylvania landscape. Built by Westinghouse for the Atomic Energy Commission, the nuclear reactor will produce at least sixty thousand kilowatts of electrical power. The Duquesne Light Company built the non-nuclear part of the plant, i.e., the turbogenerator, and contributed five million dollars to the reactor costs, the rest of the bill being paid by the AEC. This plant will go into operation in 1957, but it is not expected to provide electrical power which will compete with Pittsburgh power. It is an experimental prototype designed to provide first-hand operating experience with nuclear power stations. Nonetheless, the power produced will be distributed by the Duquesne Light Company, and the revenue will lessen the shock of the high-cost power.

The Shippingport reactor is a uranium-water design in which there is an investment of roughly one million dollars' worth of enriched uranium, or 115 pounds. This is surrounded by a blanket of about twelve tons of ordinary uranium. All of this nuclear fuel is contained in a special steel case standing three stories high and measuring nine feet across. This is the 250-ton pressure vessel manufactured by Combustion Engineering from eight-inch-thick steel lined with a half inch of stainless steel. To contain the two thousand pounds (PSI) of water pressure, the vessel's dome is fastened shut with eight-inch-thick bolts six feet long. Water is forced through the reactor core under high pressure so that it will not boil, and it is then passed through a heat exchanger or steam generator. From this point on we can forget about the nuclear origin of the heat and proceed as we would in any modern steam-electric plant. Steam turns a turbine and produces the electrical energy which is then piped out to consumers in the vicinity.

Our first atomic electricity will be very expensive. At first, it is estimated that the Shippingport plant will turn out electricity at about five cents per kilowatt hour. This is many times higher than cheap coal-produced electrical power. When a second uranium core is inserted into the pressure vessel and the power output is upped, the cost should drop to about four cents per kw-hr. This might go as low as 1.4 cents when a third core is fabricated much later. Much depends upon the eight-foot-long uranium fuel rods and how well they stand up under prolonged usage inside the reactor. If one can achieve high burnup of the fissionable fuel and leave the rods inside the reactor for a long time without discharging the rods, then costs can be trimmed.

Actually, the capital costs of the Shippingport plant are very high. Utility men usually figure costs on the basis of a kilowatt capacity. In the case of the Shippingport plant the cost per installed kilowatt will run about eight hundred dollars or more. This high figure contrasts with the estimate of a low of $220 per kilowatt which the Consolidated Edison Company of New York makes for its 250,000 kw plant. The latter is to be financed privately and will be erected on the Hudson River at Indian Point, near Peekskill. The plant site is only twenty-four miles north of New York City. Construction of the new plant will be undertaken by Babcock and Wilcox Company and is expected to be completed early in 1960. Plants like this one are expected to produce electricity at about one cent per kilowatt hour.

The heart of the Consolidated Edison plant is also housed in a huge pressure vessel but the active core inside is a 6-by-6-foot cylinder. This inner core consists of two parts: one is an assembly of enriched uranium fuel clad with Zircaloy (a zirconium alloy which prevents the uranium from being corroded by coolant water); the other is a stack of flat plates of thorium. When the reactor starts up, the chain reaction will produce heat in the uranium fuel, and this heat will produce power as in the Shippingport plant. But as the plant runs, neutrons from the chain reaction will swarm through the thorium plates. We have already seen that when neutrons irradiate U^{238} they can produce plutonium; in this case the neutrons get captured in thorium and convert it into uranium-233. The latter is just as good a fuel as U^{235} or plutonium, and as it builds up in the thorium it can, itself, start to sustain a chain reaction. We call thorium a fertile material because it can be made to produce fissionable fuel. Thus, as the Indian Point plant continues to operate, it will produce heat in the thorium plates due to the burnup of U^{233}. In other words, the plant will be producing part of its fuel—a very desirable thing from the economic viewpoint.

Can nuclear reactors be designed so that they produce more fuel than they burn? This sounds very much like perpetual motion to some people, but it is not. Actually, pilot plants have been developed which do produce more nuclear fuel than they burn up. Atomic Power Development Associates, Inc., comprising some of America's largest firms and utilities, is developing a hundred-thousand-kilowatt nuclear plant which will breed more fuel than burned. The nuclear reactor for this plant is called a fast breeder since it runs on fast or high-speed neutrons. Designed to be built at Monroe, Michigan, this plant differs quite radically from those we have just described. Walker Cisler, prominent American industrialist, is the moving force behind the daringly designed "fast power breeder."

The core of the fast breeder is only thirty inches in diameter and the same dimension in height. Its volume is only about twelve cubic feet, which is not much more than many refrigerators in home use. This small volume will contain about half a ton of partially enriched uranium. Outside the core, rods of U^{238} will act as a blanket to catch the outward-bound neutrons. U^{238} converts into plutonium, as we have explained before, and the designers calculate that the reactor could produce 240 pounds of plutonium (new fuel) per year while burning up a total of about 200 pounds of primary U^{235} fuel. Thus, one year's operation would yield a surplus of forty pounds of new fuel. Nothing even remotely comparable exists in any other non-nuclear power plants. The power breeder would, in effect, have no charges assessed against it for fuel. This would be true only if the excess fuel produced balanced out the chemical processing costs involved in treating the spent fuel rods and fabricating new ones. In practice, "zero cost" fuel is probably not attainable, but certainly the cost can be very small if the power plants can be made to breed.

This discussion of breeding may persuade the un-initiate that he is getting something for nothing—akin to perpetual motion. Actually, what is involved is a conversion of a fertile material such as thorium or uranium into a nuclear fuel. All atomic energy is based upon the small fraction (0.7 per cent) of U^{235} present in uranium: it is this stuff which is the original keystone of atomic power. Neutrons scavenged from the chain reaction fission of U^{235} can be absorbed in thorium and U^{238} to produce new nuclear fuels. Thus, breeding makes available potentially all the fission energy locked up in our thorium and uranium reserves rather than the tiny fraction stored in U^{235}.

The power breeder we have just described runs on fast neutrons, meaning that no slowing down or bumping around of neutrons is required as in machines already described. The fast breeder can therefore be made very compact and, we might add, would be attractive in an engine for propelling an aircraft. Compactness, however, raises great problems of heat transfer since the entire power production of a reactor is concentrated into such a small volume. The heat is too great to be removed by pumping a gas or ordinary liquid through the reactor core. Instead, reactor engineers resort to a more daring approach, that of circulating a liquid metal such as a sodium potassium alloy (NaK) through the heart of the reactor. Ordinarily, one thinks of this alloy as a solid metal, but it melts at low temperature and can be pumped safely by using specially designed pumps.

From what we have explained, it must now be evident that there are many different roads to follow in designing nuclear power plants. The reactors may be fast, intermediate or thermal if we specify the speed of the neutrons involved in perpetuating the chain reaction. The choice of nuclear fuel is varied, and it may be fabricated in many different ways. Indeed, it may even be prepared as a liquid or slurry. Reactors may incorporate a variety of moderators in their cores, ranging from ordinary water to heavy water or from graphite to berryllium. The choice of coolant is also manifold for one can use a gas, such as carbon dioxide which the British will use in their first plants, or a liquid such as water in the Shippingport design, or a liquid metal as in the power breeder. Reactor designers are thus given great latitude in dreaming up the plans for new nuclear power plants, and it is not surprising that units now being considered for construction vary markedly in structure.

North American Aviation, for example, has designed a sodium-graphite combination in a reactor to be built for Consumers Public District in Nebraska. The

General Electric Company is working on a novel "boiling water" reactor for the Nuclear Power Group: this unit will produce 180,000 kilowatts and will be located near Chicago. Known as the Dresden plant, it is to be completed in 1960 and will involve heat transfer from the reactor core to ordinary water, which will be boiled in the core to provide useful steam. Yankee Atomic Electric Company wants to bring nuclear power to the New England area by building a 134,000 kw A-plant in northwestern Massachusetts. Pennsylvania Power and Light Company is aiming at a 150,000 kilowatt plant of rather different design. Known as an aqueous-homogenous reactor, it will feature a solution of a uranium salt rather than fuel rods of nuclear material. If preliminary research and development provides promising results, Westinghouse will undertake construction of the plant with 1962 as the target completion date.

All of these reactors we have just enumerated provide power in large packages. Smaller package power plants are under development by the AEC, Defense Department and U.S. industry. Plants ranging in power from 2,000 to 25,000 kw are being developed to provide smaller communities with electrical power.

When these nuclear power plants have been built and the operators have had time to assess their actual power costs, based upon actual experience, we will be in a much better position to know how soon nuclear power will become competitive with other fuels. One thing is certain, nuclear power will take a long time to make much of an impact upon our over-all national economy. The transition from ordinary fuels to nuclear fuels should be very gradual and should not involve any severe dislocation of the existing economy.

Location of nuclear power plants inside city limits or very close to metropolitan areas naturally raises the question of reactor safety. Can these plants be designed to be non-explosive? Can adequate safeguards be devised to automatically shut down a defective reactor? How much risk is there to a community if a reactor should run away?

These are not simple questions to answer; in fact, they account for some of the delay encountered in the authorization of plants for construction. Nuclear reactors will not blow up like A-bombs, that is not the big worry. The danger is that controls might fail and the chain reaction would get out of hand or run away. After all, the controls are moving parts, often boron-coated rods, which slide in and out of the reactor core, depressing and accelerating the growth of neutrons in the chain reaction. All such mechanical or electromechanical systems are subject to breakdown, so that the experts who design reactors must provide safety features or alternate methods of shutdown for the reactor. No matter how ingenious a designer is, there is always the possibility of mechanical or human error and you need only one slip-up to ruin a nuclear reactor.

Should the chain reaction run away and melt part of the reactor core, some additional safeguards must be provided to prevent the escape of radioactive particles from ruptured or melted reactor components. One method for protecting the vicinity from radioactive contamination is to surround the reactor with an external shell to trap the radioactive particles. This, however, adds to the expense of the installation and makes it more difficult for nuclear power to compete with conventional power.

The Atomic Energy Commission examines all reactor designs very carefully to assess the degree of hazard that their operation might involve. The AEC has a Reactor Safeguards advisory committee composed of experts to advise it on reactor safety. These advisors are aware that the fission products produced in the A-plants are many millionfold more toxic than chlorine, the most toxic of all industrial hazards. Furthermore, they appreciate that you cannot shut off the heat from a reactor as you would flip a switch, for the split atoms of uranium keep emitting heat long after the plant is shut down. They know, moreover, that a high-power reactor, operating for a year, will contain enough radioactivity so that if it escaped in a cloud and descended nearby, people five to ten miles away might be killed or injured. One can imagine the lawsuits which might be filed by citizens who suspected that they were injured. One of my lawyer friends, with whom I discussed this problem, told me that he would always bet on a court ruling in favor of his client, if he claimed injury from radiation. For these reasons the AEC can be expected to be very judicious and conservative in evaluating the safety of any proposed reactor. In fact, so judicious that Dr. Teller joked about the advisory committee as "the reactor prevention committee."

Those who wonder what happens to all the radioactive material produced inside a nuclear reactor are justified in asking if the experts have found any good burial ground for the hot fission products. The current answer is no, but research may turn up a disposal method in the future. This waste disposal problem would be relatively simple if the split atoms of uranium were not mixed in huge amounts of chemical solutions. As it is, these solutions are stored by the AEC in big chemical tanks. By the year 2000 a robust nuclear industry may produce one ton of fission products per day; the latter will form an immense radioactive hazard. We may have to dispose of one million gallons of waste per day.

Many ideas have been advanced for disposing of these unwanted hazardous materials. Interment in desert ground, sinking in ocean deeps, pumping into dry gas wells, burial in arctic icecaps and even consigning the stuff to outer space have all been suggested. Oceanographers are strongly of the view that the wastes should be buried on land, whereas geologists strongly favor burial at sea. A group of U.S. experts feel that first choice for waste disposal should be storing the liquids in rock salt cavities. Such geological formations are very "tight" and would insure safe storage. Second choice is deep injection of the wastes into the earth between three and five miles down, where ground water would not be endangered. One suitable basin in Oklahoma, covering thirty-five acres, could store ten billion barrels of waste products providing the subterranean water were pumped out first. A third method would be to store the liquid wastes in unsaturated soils in semi-arid areas such as South America provides in a number of locations.

Whatever method is finally adopted, one thing is clear; the method must guarantee that the sanctity of the burial ground will remain undisturbed for many decades. Otherwise, there would still be sufficient radioactivity to pose a serious hazard to those who wished to use the "radioactive cemetery."

Much of the energy which man uses today is burned in propulsive devices of relatively low power. Some fifty million automobiles in the U.S.A. and several million more trucks consume vast quantities of petroleum fuels. Many million Americans own power boats, outboard motors, power lawn mowers and a hundred other small mobile devices which are rated relatively low on a horsepower yardstick. Public transportation focuses on diesel-electric trains and gasoline-driven aircraft. These things have revolutionized our modern way of life almost as much as bringing electricity into our homes and factories. We can therefore ask whether or not nuclear power will play a role closer to our everyday life than the big central station nuclear-electric plants we have described earlier.

Our discussion of military propulsion in the previous chapter paves the way for answering questions about commercial atomic aircraft, nuclear locomotives and automobiles.

If the U.S. Air Force is to have nuclear-powered bombers, may the layman not expect that these will be followed with civilian versions in the same way that military jets have served as forerunners of commercial jet transports soon to take to the skies? When this question was put to the AEC specialists in aircraft propulsion, they were quite pessimistic that commercial atomic aircraft would be feasible. The military can afford to pay premiums for transportation that civilian competitive air transport cannot countenance. Moreover, the radiation risks involved in taking off and landing a nuclear aircraft near a large city seem prohibitive in the foreseeable future. Shielding the aircraft reactor also constitutes a problem, for the plane could not be subjected to the military discipline and isolation of Air Force air bases. Again, it is a question of what the nuclear plane would do that a jet airliner would not. It would appear that the real advantage of the atom-airliner would be its longer range, but unless bored, earth-bound people wished to spend their days aloft circling the earth and chasing the sun, this unlimited range for the A-plane would not seem too great a plus mark. Jet airliners will undoubtedly develop greater range, and even presently perfected stratojets assure six-hour transatlantic crossings.

In Chapter 14 we shall be discussing a new and radically different power source, controlled hydrogen power, which may be the answer to more manageable packaged power. This is a long poke in the future, but it is all too evident that the radiation hazards linked with uranium power are very formidable and are most difficult to surmount. We do not yet know what an H-power plant would look like, but confidence is rising that this new source of energy will be harnessed.

The prospects, then, for a uranium power plant in an aircraft for commercial applications do not seem to offer material advantage over chemical propulsion, this being due to the great weight and danger associated with the nuclear reactor. Some of this current pessimism about nuclear aircraft may wane when we gain more experience with nuclear-powered flight, in the same way that successful operation of the *Nautilus* dissipated the doubts of die-hards in the Navy.

We do have nuclear-propelled submarines now at sea, and therefore we may inquire about the prospects for adapting this new driving force to commercial vessels. Admiral Rickover has given some answers which are illuminating although not very rosy-hued. "Reactor plants of the *Nautilus* type have small possibility of becoming economically feasible for commercial ships," says the hard-driving Admiral, and he goes on to explain that: "nuclear powerplants are more costly to design, build, operate, maintain, and repair than conventional powerplants. With the present state of nuclear powerplant technology, it is not possible to predict the ultimate economic feasibility of nuclear powered commercial ships."

Admiral Rickover's gloomy view of atomic ships and ocean liners is based upon a hardheaded dollars-and-cents approach to the problem, for he makes no bones about the technical possibility of harnessing A-power for ship propulsion. An estimate made available early in 1956 put the cost of a replacement *Nautilus* engine at eighteen million dollars as compared with $2.5 million for an oil-fired plant of equal horsepower. Over all, it was thought that a nuclear ship would cost two to three times as much as an ordinary oil-driven vessel. Fuel costs for the first nuclear submarine run about fifty times those for the merchant marine, and it is expected that nuclear fuel costs will drop to a half or a third of this value in five years. Here, we should point out that the nuclear engines considered are not power breeders but are burner-uppers of fissionable fuel.

Personally, I would be more optimistic than Admiral Rickover, and I think that he will change his tune ten years from now. Rick's down-in-the-mouth attitude toward commercial ship propulsion is based upon a *Nautilus* prototype engine, which is a purely military design with little thought given to economic considerations. If our industrialists are optimistic about building A-plants on land that can compete with coal-fired boilers, then I think it is reasonable to expect that economic nuclear powerplants can be developed for ocean-going ships. Somebody has to do the work and somebody has to risk some capital if the job is to be done soon. President Eisenhower intervened personally in an attempt to speed up the launching of a nuclear ship when he proposed on April 25, 1955, that a merchant ship be powered with a *Nautilus* engine to demonstrate to the world how atoms could work at peacetime applications. Congress turned back his request for funds, but the Eisenhower proposal did awake the Maritime Administration to the possibility of nuclear-powered ships. It, too, asked Congress for funds to build a nuclear ship, a twenty-two-million-dollar tanker, but this request was likewise denied, but later an A ship was approved.

Fuel is a big expense item to the nation's railroads, amounting to over a third of operating costs, so locomotive owners are justified if they intrude into the area of atomic energy, seeking a means of cutting their rising costs. The locomotive business has witnessed a startling upheaval in one decade when most steam engines were replaced with diesel-electric drives. Thousands of diesel-electric units are on order for the next few years, and one cannot blame railroad executives if they eye the atom a bit apprehensively. They have known one revolution and they are now gun-shy.

A railroad magnate picks up his copy of the *Wall Street Journal* and reads of atomic bombers; he figures if a high-power engine can be compressed into a space and weight suitable for aircraft, why couldn't a lower-power, bulkier engine be made to drive the wheels of his locomotives?

Nine rail executives descended upon the Atomic Energy Commission late in 1955 with just such a question in mind. Imagine their chagrin when they were told that information on aircraft propulsion could not be released to the railroad industry. They were also informed that the AEC had "no government program directed toward the development of nuclear-powered locomotives." However, the Army Transportation Corps had just started a study "to determine if any military requirement exists in this field." Again, the same monotonous formula in the AEC—use the military route. Had the railway executives been politically astute, they would have leaked a story to the press, stating that the Soviets had a nuclear locomotive under construction. Then, the United States would have immediately started a crash program on A-engines for rail propulsion!

Obviously, the dollars-and-cents problem is of critical concern to locomotive experts. They will not go for nuclear traction unless it promises some financial advantage over the diesel-electric drive. Right now, the capital costs for a nuclear engine look prohibitive. Furthermore, the unlimited range of an atomic locomotive is not such a great attraction to earth-bound vehicles. And the danger of a train wreck with the accompanying radioactive hazards is not pretty to contemplate. So, it is no wonder that the nine executives left Washington with little enthusiasm for atoms on the track. Again, it's a case of something that's technically possible, but, at present, economically unappetizing.

As for trackless vehicles the prospects are even dimmer. Atomic automobiles still belong to Buck Rogers and nuclear trucks or busses are equally *verboten*, again, primarily, because of the many tons of shielding required for even a modest reactor. Cutting corners on shielding is very difficult when the person to be shielded from the radiation is very close to the reactor. In the case of nuclear planes, the crew can be located at the other end of the plane and thus can be protected by both distance and by selective location of the shield.

All of the applications which we have just considered involve conversion of the atom's energy into heat and then into mechanical power. The possibilities are very remote that atomic energy can be converted directly to electrical power. As explained in Chapter 14, what we lack is the really bright idea to accomplish this trick. But we can consider using the heat produced by atomic plants without converting the heat into electricity.

Let me say at the outset that I do not have in mind individual atomic heaters which one might install in a house. These would be far too expensive to consider for home use, let alone the hazards involved in having the man of the house tinker with the atomic furnace.

What I do have in mind is the application of large reactors producing what is called "process heat" in industry. Firms which use large quantities of process heat naturally locate their plants where fuel is cheap. This means that for nuclear heat to replace coal or natural gas as a source of heat, the competition will be very stiff. But there are some industries which have to locate as nature dictates, namely, the mining concerns. Very often valuable mines are quite distant from sources of cheap power, and the transportation costs involved in shipping the bulk ore to the power source can be so high as to prohibit profitable exploitation of the mineral. Certain mining areas in South America certainly fall in this category. Bringing a nuclear plant to the minehead in mountainous regions or to the frozen "wastes" of the Antarctic, where valuable mineral deposits are thought to exist, might be the ideal solution to the mining problem.

Apart from these mining operations, there is also the possibility that nuclear heat may play an important role in the desalinification of sea water or brackish continental water. It is somewhat ironic that many places which need water most critically have huge reserves right in their front yard—California and

Texas, for example. Yet the salt in sea water makes it a forbidden fruit. Distillation of sea water to convert it into drinkable or usable water is presently undertaken in very special circumstances, such as aboard hospital ships or isolated islands, where the high price of distillation can be tolerated. However, farmers along the arid Texas Gulf coast cannot afford to pay the present costs of converting sea water into fresh water even though they have at hand some of the world's cheapest natural gas power. Nuclear heat will have to be exceedingly cheap to help the Texas farmers, but continued research and development may point the way toward cracking this tough problem. Man has yet to learn how to use the extreme temperatures and powerful radiation emitted by nuclear fission. Therefore, rather than trying to force the atom to compete with ordinary fuels, it might be smarter to dream up ways to use the unique heat and radiation given off by a nuclear reactor.

Almost all our chemistry or, more properly, our chemical engineering, of today is restricted to the relatively low temperatures attainable with gas, coal and oil. Utilization of the extremely high temperatures which nuclear fuels promise offers the potential of revolutionary new developments.

In summary, nuclear power appeared to Fermi and others as a real possibility when the chain reaction was achieved on December 2, 1942. The atom then remained within sight of scientists and engineers within the wartime project, and was largely exploited for purely military purposes. Following the war, atomic energy emerged as potentially valuable to a peacetime economy, but its development was tied to certain secret military applications. Only recently has nuclear power been actively pursued for its peacetime value, so that we are little more than just beyond the threshold of a new age of power. Almost all the applications proposed for this new source of energy are merely substitutions for those presently sustained by coal, oil and gas. The radiation hazard of nuclear reactors severely limits the present utility and range of application of uranium as a fuel. Waste products from an atomic industry present unprecedented problems, the solution of which is still embryonic.

We shall take a longer look at the future of the atom's power in the final chapter. Meanwhile, we shall look at some uses which we have found for the atom, itself; uses which are practical and which are here today.

chapter **13**

NUCLEAR INGENUITY

In the San Francisco area there is a small business outfit, the Sequoia Process Corporation, which has doubled its sales each of the past several years by simply exposing its product to the scorching power of atoms. The founders of the Redwood City company discovered that if you treat wire insulated with a plastic coating to the cross fire of rays given off by split atoms, the insulation undergoes a remarkable change. Others had known that plastics could be changed by nuclear radiation, but these industrialists working with Stanford Research Institute scientists found that the addition of a secret ingredient to the plastic was the real trick. Their plastic insulation then became extremely resistant to heat and gave the company a superior product.

Today, there are about one thousand U.S. firms which are using discarded uranium by-products in their research laboratories and industrial processes. Dr. Willard F. Libby, scientist member of the Atomic Energy Commission, estimates that these miscellaneous industrial uses for the atom save industry over a hundred million dollars each year. Each year new ingenious uses are found for the versatile atom and its potent radioactive rays which are so troublesome in nuclear power plants.

To illustrate the individual power of the atom, just think of driving your car down a highway. You

238

know that as the wheels turn and the rubber grips the highway to provide traction, friction takes its toll on the tire's rubber surface. If you drive sanely and do not burn up your rubber in scorching stops, then you many get thirty thousand miles on a set of tires just as I do. But can you imagine measuring how much rubber you wear off in traveling a short stretch of highway or in making one stop? Engineers can do this very trick by incorporating some radioactive substance in the rubber tire and following up a car with a Geiger counter. Weeks of work can be telescoped into minutes by this tracing technique using radioactive atoms.

Many pipeline companies use radioactive atoms to "tag" different kinds of petroleum which they pump through the same line. Just as one inserts a bookmark by the last page in one's reading, the engineers inject a glob of radioactive material in between two consignments of different quality oil being pumped cross country. As the oil is pumped from one state to another through the pipeline, the radioactive material is carried along in the interface between the two batches of oil. As it arrives at the distribution point, it triggers a Geiger counter and the station attendant turns the valves which divert the oil to its proper storage containers.

Research experts seeking to improve the quality of lubricating oils have found that radioactive substances provide a neat method for evaluating the lubricants. What they do is to take some piston rings and simply expose them inside a nuclear reactor, such as the one at Oak Ridge, Tennessee. Neutrons from the chain reaction riddle the piston ring and make some of the metal atoms highly radioactive. Then the rings are taken out, shipped to the research laboratory in shielded cases and carefully fitted into test pistons in a laboratory engine. Technicians then run the engine with various lubricants and measure the radioactivity worn off the piston ring. Geiger counters are so sensitive to submicroscopic amounts of radioactive material that one can easily measure frictional wear on pistons run for only a few hours. Ordinarily, such wear tests would take hundreds and thousands of hours to yield meaningful results. Using radioactive techniques, one has only to measure the uptake of radioactive particles by the lubricant.

The Ford Motor Company uses radioactive material in the form of radioactive cobalt to study the behavior of piston rings inside an operating engine. A small plug of radiocobalt is fitted into the piston ring, and researchers then follow the way in which the ring rotates as the piston flies up and down in the engine block. Not to be outdone, Soviet technicians have developed anti-friction coatings for moving parts in engines and have tested them using radioactive iron.

At the Dearborn foundry of the Ford Company there are factory-long pneumatic tubes which are used to shoot metal samples to the test lab. Sometimes the tubes get jammed, and it used to take several hours to locate the obstruction. Now all the plant maintenance people do is to dispatch a small sample of radiocobalt in a container and trace it down with a Geiger counter. This usually takes about ten minutes. More important uses for radioisotopes are found in the foundry, itself, where basic metallurgical processes are followed step by step, using a variety of atoms as "tags" to give evidence as to the location of an impurity in an alloy, the amount of this impurity and basic information about the alloying mechanism.

Rusting of iron is a troublesome and costly characteristic of the metal which has entered so profoundly into the structure of industrialized nations. No really cheap and effective mechanism has been devised to counter the oxidation of iron, so that bridges and exposed ironwork must constantly be resurfaced and repainted to protect against weathering. Development of protective coatings for iron has been largely a "salt and pepper" proposition, but a new element now gives real promise of understanding and doing something about rust. The new element is technetium, number 43, which is bracketed by molbydenum and ruthenium in the periodic system of elements. No technetium exists in nature, and for a long time it was a "missing" element. With the development of giant nuclear reactors, weighable quantities of this new element were produced as a fission product of uranium. Quite recently, it has been discovered that an exceedingly small trace of technetium inhibits rusting of iron, so that samples of the metal immersed in water do not rust if they are coated with an invisible layer of technetium. The element, technetium, is radioactive and may not be economically useful in coating of iron, but it certainly provides basic information about the oxidation process and may lead to new effective ways of controlling rust in our most widely used metal.

The "tightness" of a container is very important to

industry whether the object concerned is a vacuum pump or an underground gas storage well. Finding leaks in a system can be a most exasperating, time-consuming and expensive proposition. Modern leak-detectors have been devised using radioactive gas, such as argon, to yield the clue for finding the leak. For example, some radioargon was used to discover where leaks were occurring in a big underground gas storage depot. Radiation instruments were used to survey the field and they quickly spotted some loose well casings as being responsible for the leakage.

These are but a few of the thousands of industrial applications found for radioisotopes. The man who has done more than anyone else to encourage the wide-spread use of these materials is the dapper Dr. Paul Aebersold, who makes his home at Oak Ridge, Tennessee. Known as "Mr. Isotope," Paul is an energetic scientist-salesman who is equally adept in the laboratory and on the dance floor. Next to science, his great passion is ballroom dancing and figure-skating. After the war, the nimble-footed physicist took charge of the Isotopes Branch of the AEC and did a most remarkable job of "selling" isotopes and encouraging their use throughout the nation.

Oak Ridge served as the primary production center for radioisotopes, with the chief production facility being the air-cooled nuclear reactor we described earlier. Although the split atoms of uranium yield three dozen different elements and many more radioisotopes, these are difficult and expensive to separate out in pure form. Very often, it is more satisfactory to prepare a sample of an appropriate element and put it inside the Oak Ridge reactor to "cook." Depending upon the sample, it may have to be irradiated for days, weeks or even months. There are over eight hundred species of radioactive atoms, ranging from some which live for seconds, to many which persist for months and even to some which do not die out for many years. Each atomic species has its own characteristic time for disintegrating. Physicists use a term known as "half-life" to describe the persistence of a radioactive species. Radioactive carbon or carbon-14 has a half-life of 5,600 years and is thus long-lived. Strontium-90, as we have noted, has a half-life of twenty-eight years. Phosphorus-32, much used in medical research, exhibits a two-week half-life, whereas sodium-24 is shorter-lived, decaying with a half-period of fifteen hours.

Despite their great difference in persistence, all these species obey the same fundamental rule in decaying. If we start with a hundred radioactive units of carbon-14 (the unit is called the curie in honor of the discoverers of radium) then one half-life later, that is, 5,600 years, there will be 50 curies remaining. In another 5,600 years, this will be halved to 25 curies and so forth. The radioactivity will die out until after six half-lives there is only a small fraction of the original radiocarbon left.

Carbon-14 happens to be a most useful atom, especially since nature is generous enough to manufacture a small amount of it in the upper atmosphere. Cosmic rays smash into the atmosphere and convert some of the nitrogen into radioactive carbon. This carbon-14 is being formed today just as it was long ago, say, during the time of the pyramid builders, the eternity-loving Egyptians who sought immortality in stone. While the most obvious of their monuments does consist of stone, the ancient kings left some other relics more fragile and more revealing to us. These were the wooden sun boats or funeral ships discovered in well-sealed crypts. Dr. Willard Libby has specialized in studying radiocarbon, and he is responsible for developing a method of dating the past by taking a small chunk of wood or carbon-containing substance and analyzing its radiocarbon content. The solemn-faced and meticulous chemist took a piece of timber from an Egyptian sun boat, burned it to charcoal and then used extremely sensitive Geiger counters, shielded in a lead vault, to assay the carbon-14 content of the wood, which had been cut down centuries ago. Libby then calculated that the trees supplying timber for the sun boat had been cut down roughly eighteen centuries B.C. His deduction was based on the fact that when the trees were felled, they stopped extracting carbon dioxide from the air and thus were cut off from further intake of the slight amount of radiocarbon in the atmosphere. What Libby did was to determine how much of the original radiocarbon in the timber had disintegrated, and by fairly simple processes he figured out how long that took. His method of providing a timeclock for ancient times has been most valuable to archeologists, and there are now several research centers which routinely examine samples from all over the world and assign proper time origins to these artifacts.

Radiocarbon is also produced in the Oak Ridge

plant, and it has found many uses in biology and medicine. Carbon is an important building block in human tissue which consists of largely hydrocarbon compounds, and methods have been worked out for incorporating known amounts of carbon-14 in a wide variety of carbon compounds. It happens that the radioactive rays emitted by carbon-14 are rather weak or "soft" and are easily absorbed in aluminum foil. Radiocobalt, on the other hand, emits powerful rays which require a thick slab of lead for their absorption. Each species of atom has its own distinctive radioactive personality, distinguished by its half-life and the quality of the radiation it sends forth. Thus, the researcher has a wide choice of tools to use in the laboratory, and the engineer has also quite a number of choices among atoms which might be useful in industry. We have already discussed a number of these, but we have deliberately postponed describing perhaps the most important use industry has found for Dr. Aebersold's ubiquitous atoms.

This important industrial application for atoms consists in the use of a device known as a thickness gauge. Suppose, for example, you manufacture some sheetlike or film material which has to be a certain thickness. Paper or plastic film is a good example. Mass production technique requires that the product whiz through huge rollers or calenders at express-train speed. How can you be sure that the film thickness is both uniform and precisely what you want? You certainly do not want to stop the presses and measure the thickness, and therefore it is desirable to make your measurement on the fly. Here, the isotopes step in and give an ideal solution. By mounting a source of radioactive material above the moving film and setting up a radiation measuring instrument below the racing strip, you can easily measure how many of the rays of particles are stopped in the film. For a given film thickness, one can select just the right radioactive material and adjust the gauge so that small variations in film thickness produce easily measured electrical currents in the meter. Then, you can couple the output of this meter directly to a control mechanism driving the speeding presses so that a uniform thickness film spins off the production line. This technique is currently used to control the production of paper, plastics, cloth, floor coverings, aluminum and even cookies.

Powerful sources of radioactivity also substitute for big X-ray machines in testing castings, examining welds and checking hundreds of industrial items for flaws. Some of the waste products from our bomb production plants at Hanford, Washington, have found use in industrial radiography, but it does not appear that these uses can ever provide the solution to the waste disposal problem. Nonetheless, many promising applications for the nuclear radiation emitted by these waste products have been found, and it has been proposed that spent fuel rods from reactors might be used to irradiate and sterilize meat and other food products.

Companies such as General Foods, General Mills, Pillsbury and meat processors like Swift and Wilson are spending hundreds of thousands of dollars to investigate the effects of food irradiation. It is common knowledge that many foodstuffs are subject to rapid deterioration due to fungal and bacterial action. One of man's major advances in providing a better and more abundant way of life came from improvements in the art of food preservation. Today, U.S. food processing ranks as one of the nation's greatest industries, doing an annual business close to sixty billion dollars. Two-thirds of all U.S. food products are processed and packaged before they reach the consumer. Yet spoilage causes a very real markup in the nation's food bill, as does the need for expensive refrigeration and allied transportation of perishable foodstuffs. In some produce lines, spoilage introduces a 50 per cent loss between farm and the consumer's table.

Experiments have shown that many common foods exhibit prolonged shelf life after irradiation with penetrating atomic rays. Naturally, this does not protect the food against reinfection by bacteria or fungi, so the food must be hermetically packaged prior to irradiation. After radiation treatment, some of the foods show extended freshness even when kept at room temperature. Included in this category are green beans, bacon, asparagus, chicken and Brussels sprouts. Still other food items such as hamburger, tomatoes, beefsteaks and luncheon meat need to be kept refrigerated after radiation exposure, but they last five to ten times longer than untreated control specimens.

As with almost all new developments there are some drawbacks. These are primarily the development of off-flavor and off-odor in some of the irradiated foods and a possibility that the foods may contain toxic substances produced by the action of the radiation on hydrocarbons. The latter is the direct concern of the U.S. Public Health Service and the Food and Drug Administration.

The Army Quartermaster Corps in carrying out a long-term ten-million-dollar study of the irradiation of foods, and is co-operating with a number of government agencies and industries. It has four primary missions in investigating the effect of radiation on foodstuffs. First, the effectiveness of radiation in killing the offending micro-organisms and parasites must be clearly demonstrated. Second, the irradiated food must be shown to be wholesome and fit for continued human consumption. Third, flavor, taste and odor of the treated foods must be assured to be acceptable by consumer standards. Finally, the processing techniques must be practical from a technical viewpoint and they must be comparatively economic.

To help provide answers to the food irradiation problem, the Quartermaster Corps is planning a special three-million-dollar nuclear reactor specifically for irradiating foodstuffs. It intends to reach a pilot-plant study involving the processing of thirty tons of food per day.

It is still too early to know what the conclusions of the Army Quartermaster Corps will be, but preliminary results are promising. Pork, for example, can be treated with radiation to kill the helminthic parasite causing trichinosis, which afflicts many Americans. Some recent Public Health reports which I read showed an alarming number of sausage shipments containing this parasite. Thus, widespread irradiation of pork and pork products could virtually wipe out this parasite by interrupting its life cycle.

Research already accomplished has shown that it is feasible to kill insects infesting grain supplies by irradiating these with penetrating rays. Many nations which do not provide modern storage for their cereal crops suffer appreciable losses due to insect infestation in storage. Indeed, in tropical countries where the heat and humidity combine to make matters worse for grain storage, the losses may mount to 50 per cent. These very countries include those which live on the rim of famine, or at least do not have adequate nutritional levels for their people. Our nation, with its worries of overproduction, considers nutrition to be adequate when the male consumes 3,200 calories per day and his mate eats food averaging about 900 calories less. India, to take a horrible contrast, has a current level of about 1,700 calories per person per day. One way of increasing the caloric intake of these undernourished peoples is to preserve the food produced with minimal losses.

Another illustration of the power of irradiation is found in the treatment of potatoes to inhibit sprouting. This radiation treatment has been found to preserve the tuber so that its storage life is extended by many months and its transportation is made possible under less exacting conditions than non-treated potatoes.

These new developments show considerable promise and are certain to be watched closely by America's food processors. But the impact of the new techniques will be slow in coming, since long-term experiments are required to determine the wholesomeness of the irradiated food. It is well to underline a note of caution, for radiation is something new and radically different for food processing. During the past fifty years many new chemicals have been added to foods, and man's tolerance of this assault upon his constitution is still largely unknown. It is for this reason that a policy of watchful waiting is well advised with respect to this newest wrinkle in treating human foodstuff.

We can attack the problem of food from the point of its origin in the earth's crust. Radiation has been used to develop new strains of cereals; for example, neutron irradiation has resulted in developing a rust-resistant strain of oats. Research in North Carolina has developed a superior peanut plant, more resistant to disease and yielding 30 per cent more crop per acre. Other plants, especially cereals, have been evolved which lend themselves better to mechanical harvesting. Canada is doing a great deal of radiation work in developing new strains of superior barley.

Tagging fertilizers with radioactive atoms of calcium and phosphorus has given scientists a much better understanding of the mechanism of nutriment uptake by various plants. Fertilizers are responsible for high yields of crops such as rice in Japan, and since these soil additives are expensive, it is important to know how specific plants use the added nourishment. India, for example, produces about one-fourth as much rice per acre as Japan. If the Indians are provided with the all-important fertilizer, it will be most valuable to know how to use it in increasing crop yields.

Many aspects of agriculture are being illuminated by

the ingenious use of radioisotopes. Radiocarbon can be used to trace the growth processes in plants, and it is of basic value in understanding that most fundamental of all phenomenon—photosynthesis. Life on earth depends upon the daily receipt of sunlight which produces plant growth. Light from the sun falls upon a green leaf and sets in motion a series of imperfectly understood synthetic reactions. Researchers all over the world are seeking the answer to the puzzle of photosynthesis, and radioisotopes are proving an essential tool in their probing.

People in the United States are used to living "high on the hog," whereas the lower class in backward countries can't even eat "low"; they have to depend upon direct intake of cereals for their substance, since the indirect route of feeding cereals to cattle to produce protein is too wasteful a process. It takes on an average of seven pounds of feed to produce one pound of animal food product. The science of animal husbandry is being materially aided by the use of radioisotopes in the study of the more efficient production of animal food. Milk production in cows is undergoing the most thorough study so that a fuller knowledge of lactation processes may lead to increased milk yields.

Insect habits have been traced with radioactive atoms, and the data gathered have been used to study how plants may be protected from devastation. Efficiency of insecticides and fungicides is easily ascertained by tagging them with the proper "hot atoms," and in this way some progress is made in curtailing the three-billion-dollar annual loss which plants suffer each year.

All of these varied uses for atoms, important as they are, do not compare with the great potential value that they hold for progress in the field of medicine. Just as the microscope gave the scientists a new tool and a fresh outlook, so, too, do radioisotopes provide a new approach to the problems of human disease and bodily ills.

The human body is such a complicated machine that it is all but impossible to study the fate of a chemical or a drug administered to it, unless some means is provided for tracing the material as it courses through the blood stream and is taken up in tissue. Atoms which are radioactive are the tags which can be applied to drugs or biochemicals. Taken into the human body, these can be followed with Geiger counters. A rather simple and practical example is to be found in the case of radioiodine administered to a patient. The radioiodine or iodine-131 may be swallowed in a glass of water (newspaper name—atomic cocktail). The thyroid gland, that tiny regulating mechanism situated at the base of the throat, has a highly selective appetite for iodine, and since it cannot tell the difference between ordinary and radioactive iodine, the thyroid picks up the iodine-131 from the blood stream. Careful measurement of the radioactivity which accumulates in the thyroid gland gives an index of the state of health of that organ. Furthermore, the iodine technique reveals the presence and location of active metastases of thyroid cancer.

Many patients suffering from an overactive thyroid condition (a hyperthyroid produces excessive amounts of thyroid hormone which burns up body food at a

faster rate) may be given stiffer doses of the radioactive iodine. This localizes in the thyroid and forms
an internal source of radioactivity which bombards
the tissue much more efficiently than an X-ray beam
coming from the outside and traversing the patient's
neck. Since the iodine, administered this way, has
a half-life of eight days, the patient does not remain
radioactive very long.

The same technique may be applied in locating
brain tumors without the drastic surgical procedure
of massive removal of skull bone, for completely
automatic scanning instruments are available to trace
a picture of how the radioactivity concentrates in the
brain. A neurosurgeon may then pinpoint the location
of the tumor and proceed to extirpate it.

Medical men have been greatly aided by the rapid
growth of the Geiger counter and radiation measurement instrument business. This particular field is one
that I surveyed at the close of the war. We had developed many new instruments at the Metallurgical
Laboratory in Chicago, and we were anxious to
have private industry produce them for the peacetime
market. I made a nationwide survey of companies
which were producing Geiger counters and also those
which might be interested in doing so. There was only
a handful of small firms in the business at the time,
and their dollar volume was very small. A decade
later, we find about one hundred firms turning out
instruments for doctors, researchers and prospectors.
The Geiger counter has become a household word,
and the radiation instrument business is zooming
toward an annual forty million dollars in sales.

Four young men, all in their early twenties, who worked in our instrument section at the Metallurgical Laboratory, struck out on their own after the war. Three of them rented a small store in Chicago's South Side and pooled all their available cash to make electronic circuits for Geiger counters. This lowly venture blossomed forth to become the Nuclear Instrument and Chemical Corporation, one of the nation's leading manufacturers of radiation instruments. The fourth young man, Ernest Wakefield, set out by himself to produce Geiger counters. Today, he is president of the Radiation Counter Laboratories, which boasts of its own factory and sends high-quality counters and equipment all over the world.

One reason for the success of these companies is that the medical profession has been quick to adopt the new tool—radioactivity. Of course, radioisotopes were not the invention of the Manhattan Project, but the nuclear reactors developed during the war made possible production of a wide variety of isotopes, and the Atomic Energy Commission put the price of these within reach of almost every doctor. Furthermore, the AEC's Division of Biology and Medicine has encouraged a broad program of research, both within its own laboratories and in the facilities of our universities, colleges, and medical institutions. Much of the work sponsored by the AEC is of a fundamental and long-range nature with little possibility of immediate payoff for the practicing physician. This research is aimed at uncovering the basic mechanisms involved in life processes, for it is this knowledge which will provide the solid base for improving man's health and well-being.

Naturally, cancer looms as a towering challenge to nuclear medicine. No one knows what seemingly irrelevant piece of data will provide the clue to a new attack upon man's most feared affliction. Quite possibly the break will come where we least expect it, perhaps in a border-line field between medicine and some other discipline. But there is a growing confidence that the break will come and man will conquer his ancient enemy. This is perhaps little consolation to those who must endure the torment of cancer suffering, but even now nuclear medicine does promise some relief. I do not mean to suggest that cancer is curable. What I mean is that palliative treatment is possible.

Not long ago I was invited to speak before a distinguished group of Floridians, winter-brand, and I welcomed the opportunity to bask in Florida's warm sun in February. My host suggested that I relax before the talk by having a swim, and soon we were enjoying that exquisite massage which only a good swim can provide. I remarked about the robust health of my companion who was obviously long past retirement age, and I was astonished to learn that, six months earlier, he had been told he had only a few weeks to live. Cancer of the prostate, he said, had become so advanced as to be surgically inoperable (which is often the case with this type of cancer), but, rather than give up, he was willing to be a guinea pig. He sought out a doctor who was trying out some new techniques and underwent treatment with injections of radioactive gold. This produced dramatic relief and he was able to enjoy life once again. He knew that he had not been cured, but he was quite happy to have been helped out of his pain. To him and to thousands of others who have benefited from the atom's power, atomic energy is in the nature of a minor miracle.

Recent experimental evidence suggests that another scourge of mankind may be nearing the break point. Schizophrenia, which accounts for about half of the patients overflowing our mental hospitals, seems to have a biochemical origin. Blood, pooled from schizophrenic patients and transfused to test patient volunteers, has been shown to induce temporary or transient symptoms of the malady in mentally normal people. Dr. Linus Pauling, Nobel prizeman and the world's leading expert on protein chemistry, believes that it may be possible to lick this affliction. In tracing the biochemicals responsible for this mental malfunction, radioactive atoms will probably be vitally important. If they play only a minor role in solving this medical mystery, then they will be priceless. The cost of providing care for the mentally ill is already staggering and becomes an even greater burden upon the nation's shoulders with each passing year.

In reviewing the peacetime aspects of atomic energy, nuclear power with its multimillion-dollar installations and its novel engineering seems to dominate the scene. But closer examination shows that the individual uses of applied radioactivity, while small in particular, add up to tremendous potential for the future. Dollar-wise comparisons are faulty, and I am afraid that you cannot talk about electrical kilowatts and relief of human misery in the same breath. The promise of atomic energy, in my opinion, is limited only by man's ingenuity.

chapter 14

HYDROGEN—THE ULTIMATE IN POWER

The quest for unlimited energy was revealed to the world in a most dramatic unveiling. It came quite un-expectedly on the tenth anniversary of Nagasaki. I was lucky in being on the spot and can report this tidbit of history.

It was the opening day of the Atoms-for-Peace Conference at Geneva. The scene was the Great Hall of the ornate Palais des Nations overlooking Lake Geneva. Flags of seventy-three nations were cavorting in a fresh breeze as though sensing a new atmosphere in the Palais—where the League of Nations had its home.

Well over a thousand delegates crowded into the main chamber of the sprawling Palais, turban-be-decked scientists mingling with cosmopolitan physi-cists from western Europe. When seated, a half-dozen Latin American representatives clad in military garb stood out in striking contrast to the civilian uniformity of the assembly.

Leaning forward, I clicked the multilingual trans-lating set to "English," adjusted my earphone (needing only one since my left ear was decommissioned years ago) and waited for President Homi Bhabha to begin his opening address. It was a tense moment. For six-teen years nations had kept the atom locked up. At last the moment was at hand for scientists to again resume the cherished tradition of talking freely with one another.

Dr. Bhabha arose and approached the cluster of microphones.

"The historical period we are just entering in which atomic energy released by the fission process will supply some of the power requirements of the world may well be regarded one day as the primitive period of the atomic age," were his words which startled the delegates, unaccustomed to thinking of atomic energy as "primitive." The dark-skinned, glossy-haired Indian physicist continued, "It is well known that atomic energy can also be obtained by a fusion process as in the H-bomb, and there is no basic scientific knowledge in our possession today to show that it is impossible for us to obtain this energy from the fusion process in a controlled manner. The technical problems are formidable, but one should remember that it is not yet 15 years since atomic energy was released in an atomic pile for the first time by Fermi. I venture to predict that a method will be found for liberating fusion energy in a controlled manner within the next two decades."

Had the suave Dr. Bhabha tossed a small A-bomb in the press section, he could scarcely have produced a greater impact. From that moment on, the gentlemen of the press focused their eyes on the possibility of hydrogen power—limitless energy from the substance of the sea!

Behind the scenes at Geneva, the American delegation was shaken by Bhabha's disclosures. There was a tacit agreement between the Russians and the Americans to keep discussion of fusion power off limits. Now the fat was in the fire. This smoked out the Atomic Energy Commission, for Admiral Lewis L. Strauss, chairman of the Atomic Energy Commission, proceeded to give a press conference. I squeezed into the conference room and scribbled furiously as the Admiral parried the questions of an anxious press. Yes, the United States had a thermonuclear power project. No, details could not be given; the project was highly secret. No. H-power was not just around the corner. Cocking his head toward the ceiling, the Admiral executed a slow radar track with his eyes as though looking for an answer. He didn't expect it in his lifetime. And so it went until a rattlesnake whirring sounded in the mike—the Admiral's wrist alarm sounded, and he hurriedly asked to be excused to return to the floor of the assembly (I noted that he seemed relieved that the press conference had ended).

The next morning I prowled through the main foyer of the Palais and joined a group of top-ranking physicists having a heated discussion of H-power. The lofty-browed Dr. Hans Bethe towered over his colleagues. One theoretical physicist remarked that none of the ideas brought up by Dr. Bhabha or Admiral Strauss were the basis for applied hydrogen fusion. "They talked about the things we know won't work," he snorted.

"How long do you think it will take?" I injected into the conversation.

"It may take twenty or thirty or a hundred years," replied Bethe. "Nobody knows how to do it. We need a new approach. The things we've tried don't work." Reminding him of Dr. Bhabha's prediction of ten or twenty years produced intense irritation, and I gathered that the two great scientists did not see eye to eye.

That afternoon I walked down the hill from the Palais grounds enjoying the waterfront sights of Geneva. Just as I was flipping a mental coin to see if I would go swimming, a Volksvagen zoomed to the curb, and my friend Nabokoff, the composer from Paris, offered me a lift. He had Dr. Houtermans in tow, and soon we were discussing H-power. Over cocktails on the patio of the Hotel du Rhone, Dr. Houtermans transported us back in time to the birth of the idea which later grew into the H-bomb.

A year before the great crash in Wall Street, Dr. Houtermans was deeply absorbed in wondering about the source of energy in stars. A twinkle appeared in his deep-set eyes as he interjected, "Oh, I was doing other things, too. I was courting a very pretty girl." Explaining that he had to rule out chemical energy as the source of heat in stars, he hit upon the idea of energy from a thermonuclear process—heat evolved from the violent action of atoms deep inside the fiery furnace of a white-hot star. Convinced that he was on the right track, the young scientist and his colleague Professor d'E. Atkinson announced the discovery. One night with the stars shining in the heavens, he pointed toward the stars and exclaimed to his girl, "I know what makes them shine." Her blank stare of befuddlement convinced the scientist that he was carrying science too far—at least, for the moment.

Houterman's eyes clouded over as he recalled the

past. Knowing something of the incredible torture he endured in Soviet concentration camps, I could appreciate why bygone days troubled him. I marveled at his ability to survive such cruelty and still maintain a sense of humor, for he certainly had that. He joked over his scotch and soda and seemed a little amused that anyone should be interested in his recollections. H-bombs seemed farthest from his thoughts, but he said, "Of course, they say the Americans have made the hydrogen bomb. I don't know anything about it, but I would guess they start with an A-bomb and add some lithium to it. Lithium deuteride seems to be it." Pausing for a gulp of his drink, he added, "Then they add, I think, a coat of ordinary uranium." I made a mental note to give him an "A" for accuracy, but I hastened to ask him for his views on controlled H-power.

"I haven't looked into the matter recently," he began, "but I don't see any way to do it. Maybe there is. I don't know. But you can't contain anything at solar temperatures. It might be done with a pulsed method —as a controlled evolution of heat." With a radiant smile he concluded, "I simply don't know."

The man who started it all doesn't know. Nor does Dr. Bethe profess to know. And the eminent Hans Bethe should know, if anyone does.

It was Bethe who picked up the original idea about solar (after all, our sun is merely a star) energy. Houtermans, together with his colleague Professor Atkinson, had reasoned that inside our sun hydrogen atoms might fuse together to form helium. They knew that it would take four hydrogen atoms sticking together to form a single helium atom. It was Hans

Bethe who, ten years later, figured out just how this might work. During this decade physicists had gleaned much knowledge by working with cyclotrons and thus simulating solar conditions—in fact, far outdoing the temperatures of fifteen million degree centigrade deep in the sun's core.

The ingenious Dr. Bethe was stimulated to look into the matter through ideas which developed in conference with astronomers. He put two and two together and got four. That isn't quite correct the way Bethe calculated it, but nonetheless it's close to the truth.

Deep inside our sun, ninety-three million miles away from us, lies buried the mystery of our sun's prodigious source of energy. Dr. Bethe fashioned the key which unlocked this mystery. He knew that vast quantities of hydrogen were squeezed together by the sun's oppressive outer mantle until the hydrogen was no longer a gas but was rather a soupy paste about eight times heavier than solid lead. These hydrogen atoms were constantly thrown at each other, impelled by the fifteen million-degree heat. What Bethe did was to figure out how often hydrogen atoms would stick together. He came up with the bright idea of a carbon cycle whereby the carbon atom acted as a host for the gradual collision buildup of four hydrogen atoms into a single helium atom. His calculations checked with the observed rate of heat production in our sun; all of which made both Dr. Bethe and the astrophysicists very happy.

No one was dreaming that this happy event, the solving of one of nature's darkest mysteries, would have appalling consequences for mankind. No one, certainly not Dr. Houtermans, dreamed that an H-bomb was just below the scientific horizon.

From what we know, we should be talking about the H-bomb in quotes since it is really a super uranium bomb. But it is an irony of fate that both the A- and H-bomb were misnamed. The A-bomb became the atomic bomb, whereas in the strict technical sense it should be called the nuclear bomb. President Truman is responsible for the misnomer.

Naturally, when we trouped back from the atoms-for-peace meeting in Europe, everyone was eager to learn about the H-project in the U.S.A. Senator Clinton P. Anderson, chairman of the august Joint Committee on Atomic Energy (eighteen Congressional watchdogs), broke the ice by coming out for a more vigorous thermonuclear power program. The former Secretary of Agriculture criticized the AEC's effort, charging that less than thirty million dollars was being spent on a project that could be one of history's greatest milestones. Significantly, he concluded, "If the Russians tame the hydrogen bomb before we do they would deal a devastating moral blow to our Nation and might bring many small countries friendly to us within the orbit of Russian influence."

Inside the AEC there was ferment. Behind the white façade of the Commissions' headquarters on Constitution Avenue officials scurried to reply to the stinging criticism. Nuclear scientists, on the other hand, were pleased as Punch over the whole affair. They had alternately argued and pleaded with the Commission to take the wraps off H-power. Most of the scientists stated flatly that the whole business never should have been labeled secret in the first place. But *Secret* it was. It is understood that Admiral Strauss had upheld the order classifying thermonuclear power research, even though top scientists like Dr. Bethe had urged completely free and unfettered research. Everything about U.S. hydrogen power taming was so secret that the only thing out in the open was the fact that the AEC did have a project. And this admission was courtesy of Dr. Bhabha.

Washington and the nation waited to see the outcome of this clash between the Admiral and the Senator. It looked like a case of the immovable object and the irresistible force. The adamant Admiral might have remained glued to his holdfast had it merely been Senator Anderson in opposition. But public opinion gravitated to the Senator's side.

On October 3, 1955, the Atomic Energy Commission gave way. It revealed that its Project Sherwood had been working on H-power for several years. Work was going on a number of different sites, but it seemed that the heart of the project was contained in Project Matterhorn directed by the brilliant Professor Lyman Spitzer, Jr., at Princeton University. The forty-one-year-old astronomer, noted for his researches in astrophysics, pinpointed the problem: "By far the greatest reserve of stored energy on earth is locked up in the nuclei of hydrogen atoms present in the oceans." Calling attention to "thermonuclear burning" of hydrogen in the sun, Dr. Spitzer stated: "Thermonuclear burning occurs most readily with deuterium, a heavy isotope of hydrogen. Although only one deuterium nucleus is present in water for every 6,400 nuclei of ordinary hydrogen, the total amount of deuterium available in the ocean is enormous." On the conservative side, he estimated: "The deuterium in the ocean's waters is sufficient to provide many times the present rate of world energy consumption for more than a billion years."

Here, then, was the quest. Unlimited energy in the offing—right in the sea. As might be expected, a rash of pie-in-the-sky predictions broke out. Overheard in the United Nations and reported in the *New York Times*: "We shall be able to go to the Hudson River, scoop up a can of water, put it in the fuel tank and drive away. . . ." It was even argued that research on uranium power was old-fashioned and a waste of time.

Let's look at some of the problems involved in wringing power from light elements.

I use the term "light elements" rather than hydrogen advisedly. Dr. Spitzer singled out hydrogen and, specifically, deuterium or heavy hydrogen, but I would rather keep the door open to other candidates, too. Some scientists are fond of remarking that the unwritten Law of Thermodynamics is: "The unexpected usually happens." It certainly did in the case of the so-called H-bomb. So, perhaps, caution is dictated in assessing the future of fusion power. Among the light elements in the running are beryllium and lithium. Call them long shots, but let's keep them on the track. Meanwhile, we shall focus attention upon the favorite —hydrogen.

Before we plunge into the problem of harnessing H-power, let's take a quick look at prices. Water, as everyone knows, is H_2O. Two parts of hydrogen for every one of oxygen. But this "H" is the symbol for ordinary hydrogen (technical name: protium). Dr. Spitzer pointed to deuterium, chemical symbol "D," as the choice fusion material. This deuterium occurs in combination with oxygen in a form which we call heavy water. Getting heavy water out of ordinary water used to be quite a stunt, but the war changed all that. We needed tons and tons of heavy water for nuclear power plants. As a result the United States developed remarkably cheap ways of extracting the heavy water from river water.

The market price for heavy water used to be ninety-two dollars per pound—most of it being sold by Norway which used its abundant hydropower to produce it. At the Geneva Conference in 1955 the United States astonished everyone by quoting a new cut-rate price of twenty-eight dollars per pound. At the same time it announced a price tag of eighteen dollars for a pound of ordinary uranium. This single pound of uranium equals the power of somewhat more than two million pounds of coal.

A single pound of heavy water, about two cupfuls, would liberate power equal to about four hundred thousand pounds of coal. In other words, on a pound for pound basis, heavy water would yield about five times less energy than uranium. The assumption here is that two heavy hydrogen atoms fuse together to form a single helium atom. Contrary to what is probably assumed by the ordinary person, hydrogen fusion produces far less energy per fusion than does a single uranium fission. There happen to be a variety of ways in which hydrogen atoms can stick together, but if we consider the one which releases the most energy, the fusion process still releases over ten times less energy than a single fission process!

Our cost comparison here involves the weight of uranium or hydrogen. A single pound of heavy water contains over ten times as many atoms as does a pound of uranium. That's why the energy comparison is not even more lopsided in favor of uranium. Even though a single uranium atom is much more potent than a combining pair of hydrogen atoms, the uranium atom is so massive that there are fewer of them per pound.

If we do not narrow our choice down to hydrogen but admit lithium into the competition, then the odds go up. Consider, for example, the combination of lithium and heavy hydrogen (technically called lithium deuteride). This is really a potent package. A single pound of this stuff outranks even uranium. One pound, in fact, adds up to more power than a three-thousand-*ton* pile of coal.

All this is very reassuring. The power is there ready to be tapped; all we have to do is find the way to do it. We have to surmount some very high barriers on the road to this new power source. Dr. Spitzer has summarized the problem:

Thermonuclear burning occurs only at enormous temperatures, above a hundred million degrees Fahrenheit. Such temperatures have hitherto existed only at the centers of very hot stars or during the explosion of an atomic bomb. To convert the inexhaustible supply of energy in the earth's deuterium into useful power, we must achieve such temperatures in a gas confined within walls that remain relatively cool. We must control the thermonuclear reaction when it occurs. We must extract the energy released and use it to generate electricity.

A nice tidy little problem—merely duplicate the conditions inside our sun or an A-bomb and keep them perking for hours, days and years. No wonder a ten- or twenty-year time scale is assigned to Project Sherwood.

In approaching this thorny problem, we must be guided by a number of precedents. First, we should recall the unexpectedly rapid development of the A-bomb. Second, we should remember that the H-bomb was once allocated to a limbo somewhere "between the possible and the probable." Initial despair over the toughness of the task ahead should be tempered with optimism that equally hard jobs in the past have been accomplished. Perhaps this is what Sir John Cockcroft has in mind when he says: "My faith in the creative ability of the scientists is so great that I am sure that this will be achieved long before it is essential for man's needs." As head of the British atomic research effort, Sir John has a reputation for being a hardheaded realist in addition to being a top-flight scientist. In this case, I suspect that Dr. Cockcroft has something up in his sleeve. Americans have known for some time that the British were up to something in thermonuclear power, but because there is a high wall of secrecy between Britain and the United States we can't find out anything more than that the British have been devoting considerable effort to fusion research.

Man's accomplishments in winning power from chemical fuels such as coal, oil and natural gas are all in the province of low temperature engineering. So, too, is our current program in deriving energy from uranium. We are limited to temperatures in the range of a few thousand degrees fahrenheit. Strict limits are imposed by the firebox and heat exchange materials; they have to be kept cool enough so that they do not lose their structural strength and collapse. Jumping from a few thousand to over a hundred million degrees looks like an almost insurmountable barrier.

A clue to how the obstacle may be hurdled is to be found in one word in Dr. Spitzer's statement of the problem. It is the word "gas." The dynamic young astrophysicist is a stickler for accuracy and he uses words carefully; therefore, we had better pay attention to what the word implies. Clearly, if one had to solve the H-puzzle by developing a container to hold a *solid* material at solar temperatures one might just as well ask an armless man to untie the Gordian knot.

Let's try a new approach. What do we really mean by "temperature"? Ordinary experience shows that a solid, say, a poker of iron, glows when it gets hot. Stick it in a fire and it will turn a dull red, then a cherry red as it gets hotter, and finally white hot. We associate a certain temperature with the poker as it gets hotter and hotter. In so doing we have a pretty rigid concept of temperature. Now consider not a solid but a gas. For example, let's examine a glass tube which contains a small amount of gas—a neon discharge tube is a perfectly good example. You can take one of these reddish-glowing tubes which are so much in evidence in advertising and wrap your fingers around it without feeling much heat. The glass tube surface is relatively cold. Yet inside the tube the atoms of neon are dashing around with fantastic speed. We could just as well substitute hydrogen for neon. This would mean that atoms of hydrogen must inevitably collide at high speed—the basic requirement of a thermonuclear reaction.

This apparent paradox of the gas atoms possessing high speed (equivalent to high temperature) while remaining in the confines of a cool glass container is easily explained by the physicist. The layman has only one kind of temperature—that of a glowing hot poker. The physicist has that kind plus a second—we may call it kinetic temperature, meaning temperature associated with fast-moving particles in a gas.

Cyclotrons whirl atomic particles around and around until they attain very high energy. The latter is measured in terms of a special unit called the electron volt of energy (which the reader need not attempt to comprehend; it is introduced merely for comparison). Even cyclotrons of prewar vintage accelerated atoms to millions of electron volts. Using very simple mathematics, the physicist is able to translate electron volts to temperature. It turns out that one electron volt equals somewhat more than ten thousand degrees centigrade. This drastic markup means that a ten-million-volt hydrogen atom (hurled around in a cyclotron) has a "temperature" of a hundred billion degrees. Quite a temperature! Much more than is needed for thermonuclear reactions.

Working the problem the other way around; if we take a temperature of a hundred million degrees centigrade, it will correspond to an energy of only ten thousand electron volts. This is so low that it is really embarrassing. Cyclotrons are simply too high-powered for such low-energy work. It may sound odd, but thermonuclear research is "low-energy" to nuclear physicists! Most nuclear researchers do not stoop to such trivial energy, and that's one reason why the thermonuclear field needs exploration.

Actually, research in H-power is in a kind of no-man's land. It's too high for physicists interested in ordinary heat measurements and it's too low for the cyclotron men. Such an in-between research field is often the most difficult to explore, and this seems to be the case for fusion power.

So far we may have made the whole concept of fusion more plausible, but we have not solved the basic problem—namely, the design of a thermonuclear machine. That is the job which is being tackled by researchers in this country, in Britain and in Russia as well. A top Soviet nuclear scientist, Professor Igor Kurchatov, visited Britain's atomic research centers in the spring of 1956 and startled the scientists there by giving a lecture on what Russia was doing in harnessing H-power.

Distinguished by a luxuriant, chest-touching beard, the astute Kurchatov revealed details of the Soviet work on H-power and very politely distributed copies of his speech. A copy found its way to the Atomic Energy Commission headquarters in Washington and Dr. Edward Teller, the famed H-bomb expert, was consulted to appraise its significance.

Hungarian-born Edward Teller is known to have interpreted the Kurchatov speech of April 25, 1956, as being of the greatest importance, indicating a high degree of technical competence within the Soviet H-project. Dr. Teller argued within the high-level circles of the AEC that the United States should break its secrecy on the Sherwood Project. Many of us felt that this would happen on June 8, 1956, the date when Dr. Teller was slated to speak before the American Nuclear Society in Chicago.

I flew from Washington, D.C., to Chicago to hear Teller's exposé of our H-work and was disappointed when, speaking at a press conference in Chicago's Palmer House, he smiled apologetically and said: "I cannot tell you anything new—only review what is known." An animated and dynamic performer, the bushy-eyebrowed professor proceeded to explain the elements of fusion power, pinpointing the problem as the construction of a "magnetic bottle" ingeniously devised to "contain" completely ionized hydrogen gas.

After the newsless press conference, Teller gulped down a quick lunch and walked across the hall to deliver his lecture to the one thousand scientists and engineers attending the conference. Unknown to him, a copy of Kurchatov's complete speech (a preprint from *Nucleonics* magazine) had been placed on every seat in the auditorium. Inevitably, Teller's words would be compared with those of Kurchatov, but the *Nucleonics* preprint gave everyone a chance to make an on-the-spot comparison. As we listened to Teller saying much less than what Kurchatov had told the British at Harwell, we felt not only short-changed but chagrined that it was a man from behind the Iron Curtain who had to enlighten the Free World on controlled hydrogen power.

This is perhaps the most puzzling thing about our H-project. It is freely admitted that the project may take decades for success. Admiral Strauss has revealed: "We, and other nations as well, are seeking the elusive 'big idea' which will afford the key to this revolutionary secret." Yet the project is kept ultrasecret. It is apropos to relate a conversation I had with J. Robert Oppenheimer. I had gone to him with a problem which was a perplexing one. His advice: "When you don't know where to turn, make noises. Somebody will help you out." This certainly applies to our hydrogen project today.

When you are hunting for ideas it makes little sense to pick out a few scientists and seal them up with only their own ideas. You need to take advantage of the total resources of the whole scientific community. In fact, when the Massachusetts Institute of Technology was approached by the AEC to participate in Project Sherwood, MIT turned down a lush contract. In testimony which was given March 8, 1956, before a Congressional committee, an MIT spokesman explained that secrecy and progress in the applied H-power field were incompatible. The spokesman, Dr. M. Stanley Livingston, is a scientist with over a score of years devoted to nuclear research. He urged declassification of Project Sherwood to allow the inward flow of good ideas and suggestions.

It is the duty of Senator Anderson's Watchdog Committee to keep tab on the AEC. When he received numerous complaints from scientists about unnecessary secrecy on H-power, Senator Anderson began putting the pressure on the Commission. He addressed a letter to Admiral Strauss (made public January 24, 1956) in which the latter was challenged to defend his policy of secrecy on thermonuclear power. The Senator's attack was adroit; it knocked the props out from under the Admiral's case. The scientists would not back him up so he looked to his lawyers. After much midnight-oil-burning, the AEC rationalization of H-power secrecy emerged. Admiral Strauss stated: "If the declassification of the entire thermonuclear research were to add the missing part of the research carried on on this subject by an unfriendly power and that as a result they were able to manufacture special nuclear material in quantities, this would in my opinion impair the common defense and security of the U.S."

What this amounts to is that we might unknowingly give the missing piece of the jigsaw to the Soviets. With it they might construct a thermonuclear power plant. With the new plant they might produce bomb material of the type which we produce (and they, too) by the ton. Classifying something you haven't got on the basis that it might possibly produce something you already have got is, it seems to me, an exceedingly curious procedure.

I think that before long Project Sherwood will see the light of day. In the end rationality must prevail. Then I believe that the various disciplines of science will converge upon the harnessing of fusion energy. Very likely some odd idea, seemingly unrelated to the subject, will provide the clue for the right road to take. The history of science is replete with examples illustrating how breakthroughs in knowledge occur when a scientist toys with ideas of diverse complexion. Then the bright idea is sparked.

No one can tell when this germinal idea will develop. It may spring up next month, or next year or perhaps ten years from now. But the chances of early birth get better as more and more people puzzle over the project.

Thus, it is still too early to even sketch in the outlines of a thermonuclear device for generating electricity. Nonetheless, we can discern some advantages for this new power source. Or shall we say potential advantages since it is all in the future. One big plus mark for H-power may be its compactness in size as compared with uranium power generators. This we expect to follow from the fact that the radiation shielding problem should be of a different scale. In the case of uranium fission, we get split atoms which are immensely radioactive. These fission products make mandatory huge shields around the plant and many safeguards to protect people from accidental exposure to the poisonous effects of the split atoms. Fission is like a grievous wound which refuses to heal. Fusion, on the other hand, is a "healing" of two atoms into a single stable non-radioactive entity. All of which makes for much easier design of power plants utilizing light elements.

Another advantage links to the potential small size of hydrogen plants. It may be possible to design small package H-plants which are efficient in the production of power. If so, this will put H-power into a different bracket as compared with U-power. Uranium power plants have intestinal characteristics which make them most efficient in large economy sizes. That's why most U-plants being constructed by industry are of jumbo proportions—being capable of producing more than a hundred thousand kilowatts of electrical power. Such plants may be ideal for cities, but they freeze out the small rural community and, of course, make no impact upon really small package power use. The latter includes rural power plants, small industrial electrical generators, mine stations and a host of similar installations; these combine to add up to a significant fraction of the power production in the U.S.A.

Both of these advantages assume that H-power will be in the form of heat. Such is the case with uranium power. Hope that the uranium atom might yield its energy in the form of electricity faded at the Geneva atomic conference in the summer of 1955. The best brains of the world were gathered together to ponder over the direct conversion of U-power to electrical power. Result: no bright ideas. The same may be true for H-power, but Dr. Teller thinks that a way may be found to produce electrical energy directly. If this can be done efficiently, then hydrogen will, indeed, loom as a superior fuel although by no means a costless one. Barring some unforeseen breakthrough, it appears that uranium power is not obsolete but may be supplemented by fusion power.

Obviously, the superabundance of hydrogen as fuel for H-plants will solve man's fuel problems as long as Homo Sapiens remains on this planet. This is especially important if we look beyond the rim of this century. As long as we are taking a long view, we should emphasize that H-power will produce no toxic uranium ash, which will constitute a severe challenge when the world is populated with hundreds of nuclear power stations. Disposing of the radioactive waste is an unsolved problem even after almost two decades of research. Imagine what the problem would be like if uranium were to displace coal as the world's major source of power. Man and radioactivity do not seem to be the happiest of partners on our earth. We can only hope that there will be room for both.

Getting back to fundamentals, let's be clear about one thing. Man is just scratching the surface of the atom's energy. Whether it's the uranium atom or the hydrogen atom makes little difference. The energy man can extract is pitifully small compared with the locked-up energy beyond his reach. We have to go back to Dr. Einstein to explain just what's involved.

When a big uranium atom splits into two fragments, the hunks which hurtle apart ten thousand times faster than a rifle bullet are still sizable atoms in themselves. For example, a single fission may convert an atom of uranium into an atom of barium and an atom of krypton. The barium and krypton atoms weigh slightly less than the original uranium atom; it is this slight difference of mass which is available as energy in fission. Actually, the total number of "particles" in the original U-atom is the same as the total of the two split atoms. The energy that man can scratch at is only one-thousandth of that "contained" in the bulk of the atom. And man can grasp this one-tenth of one per cent only if he is one hundred per cent efficient in harnessing the atom's energy. Usually man scores about 25 per cent instead of 100, so that he touches only one four-thousandth of the U-atom's energy.

Hydrogen fusion is just the opposite of uranium fission. Yet the processes have this much in common. Both fission and fusion involve a slight loss of weight. Suppose two heavy hydrogen atoms stick together to form a single helium atom. The end product helium weighs slightly less than the total weight of the combining partners. Again, it is this difference which is available as energy. Einstein's relation between mass and energy, the famous $E = mc^2$ rule, is such that even a tiny bit of mass equals a great glob of energy. In the case of hydrogen fusion the percentages are a little higher than for uranium fission but they are in the same ball park. So even with H-power, man again just scratches the surface. Beneath lies the untouchable core energy which even nature keeps inviolate. Let us hope that man is content with scratching.

chapter 15

THE NEW WORLD

"This discovery begins a new era in the history of civilization. It may some day be more revolutionary in the development of human society than the invention of the wheel, the use of metals or the steam engine. Never in history has society been confronted with a power so full of potential danger and at the same time so full of promise for the future of man and for the peace of the world." Thus begins a special report by a Joint Committee of Congress.

You might jump to the conclusion that it was a report of the Joint Committee on Atomic Energy. On the contrary, the prophecy dates back to 1875 when a Joint Committee on the Horseless Carriage met to forecast the probable impact of the internal-combustion engine. The report even pointed to "the menace to our people of vehicles hurtling through our streets."

But even the farsighted Congressmen who wrote so shrewdly of things to come certainly never envisaged the huge automobile industry of today, or the vast network of concrete and macadam which crisscrosses our nation, or fifty million motorcars on these highways. Nor could they have foreseen the huge rubber factories, the sprawling empire of petrochemical plants supplying fuel and lubricants, and the roadside kingdom of filling stations.

We are little more than past the first milestone in the nuclear era. Our estimates of what 1965, 1980 and the year 2000 will bring will undoubtedly fall short of the mark, largely because we have such a small peephole through which to appraise the future. Since we very clearly would not have foretold the pace of events in the case of the automobile, how can we hope to find any guidelines to the future? Experts are almost always too conservative in their estimates. Too often they see the thorny difficulties to overcome, whereas they do not glimpse the breakthroughs which smash through many barriers at a single blow.

Yet we can make some timid projections to the future based upon man's past and present need for power, which, as we have seen, is the paramount single-package dividend of atomic energy.

Power has made man master over nature. Restricted to his own muscle power, man is a puny creature capable of generating about forty watts of power. But he has learned to extract fuels from the earth's surface to increase his power, until today he commands control over a vast new domain. The United States could not have risen to its pre-eminent pinnacle of success had it not been for the fossil fuels; the thick, gleaming veins of coal, the huge reserves of petroleum and the great wealth of natural gas. Industrialization has proceeded hand in glove with production of electrical power, largely from the combustion of these fossil fuels. In the U.S.A. electrical production has doubled every decade, until at the present time the nation is headed toward the consumption of six hundred billion kilowatt hours of electricity per year.

If our forty-watt American male works an eight-hour day five days a week, he produces a year's total of roughly seventy kilowatt-hours of energy. This is fifty times less energy than he uses in his home, his factory, and in his community in the form of electricity. And, of course, he uses much more energy in non-electrical form when he drives his car, heats his home or stokes the fires of industrial furnaces. This critical dependence upon energy has provided him with many conveniences and what we now know as luxuries. Moreover, we know that each generation will continue to make greater demands upon the production of energy.

The two big producers of energy in the U.S.A. are coal and oil, with natural gas coming up fast. Coal is becoming increasingly difficult to mine, even though reserves are very great. Furthermore, costs keep going up because of the high labor costs and difficulty of transportation. Petroleum is a superior fuel from the standpoint of production, distribution and utilization. This preferred fuel is currently consumed in the United States at the rate of three billion barrels per year. Each year, more automobiles, more tractors, diesel engines and a myriad of internal-combustion devices demand more and more liquid fuel. So far we have burned up about fifty billion barrels of oil since we started using the premium fuel.

How much more petroleum have we left below ground in the U.S.A.? The estimated reserves of the black liquid are subject to uncertainty; if you are inclined to pessimism, it's about fifty billion barrels, and about twice that figure if you are an optimist. The point is, however, that sooner or later demand will outrun supply on the domestic scene. New reserves of oil which are uncovered only postpone this day of reckoning a few years, at most. This means that unless new sources are found to supply this oil, the United States will face a critical situation.

A new source which looks promising is extraction of oil from the vast deposits of oil shales, most of which are in Colorado. Recent estimates place the U.S. oil shale reserves as containing about five hundred billion barrels of liquid fuel or five times more than our optimistic estimate of the remaining petroleum reserves. Future development must decide whether the oil can be recovered from the oil shales on an economic basis. My own opinion is that our domestic demand for petroleum is so great and the fuel is so immediately useful in so many applications, that we ought to be putting a much higher priority on oil shale research.

Even allowing for success in exploiting the oil shales, we know that man's mounting energy demands can drain the oil reserves very quickly. An annual consumption of ten billion barrels of oil per year is projectable on the basis of past trends. Indeed, one would expect this to occur before the end of this century. Figures such as these are scarcely encouraging for the long haul in the future; they compel close examination of all alternatives for filling the fuel bins of the next generation.

Conservative estimates of the uranium recoverable from known ores put their energy content at twenty times that of all fossil fuels presently in the earth's crust. In addition, very low-grade uranium ores might be exploited by refinements in mineral processing. In fact, ordinary granite contains about five parts per million of uranium—equal to thirteen times its own weight in coal. Research which has skirmished with the problem of recovering uranium from granite indicates that this might be accomplished, although it would not be economic by present standards.

But long before we would be forced to scrounge for uranium in granite, I am sure that the controlled production of power from light elements will have been achieved. We are in the predawn of H-power, and, until there is more light, we are in no position to judge the economic potential of this elemental power source. There is sufficient illumination of the uranium power situation to be fairly optimistic that uranium will compete with conventional fuel. The first round of industry's nuclear power plants may not do the trick, but men such as Detroit Edison's Walker Cisler are convinced that the atom will be our best fuel source for the future. If the daring power-breeder reactor, which Cisler is backing, is built and performs up to par it will be the forerunner of power plants which pay their own fuel bill by breeding more fuel than they burn. The far-sighted Detroit industrialist also has great hopes for the international atom and heads up an organization called the Fund for Peaceful Atomic Development, Inc., which seeks to implement President Eisenhower's atoms-for-peace proposal on a private footing. Its purpose, as stated by Walker Cisler, is: "to put to work all of the private resources available in this country and abroad so as to improve the welfare of men and women throughout the world and raise their living standard by means of atomic energy."

When we look abroad we find a vastly different

power picture from that in the United States. Only one nation tops us in per capita electrical power production, and that is Norway with its abundant, easily tapped water power and its meager population of 3.5 million. Elsewhere, countries are less well off, with France having less than a third the U.S. per capita electrical production; Spain about one-ninth that of the U.S.; Egypt sixty times less and India limping along with 160 times less electrical power per person than the U.S. India, with her teeming millions, produces less electricity per year than we burn up at Oak Ridge in producing the annual output of bomb material.

We have stressed the fact that a high standard of living and a high industrial output go hand in hand with abundant electrical power. Since uranium promises plentiful electricity in the long run, one might be tempted to think that nuclear power will be the salvation of backward nations like India, Pakistan and undeveloped regions of South America. As a matter of fact some underdeveloped nations actually have good low-cost hydropower sites but lack the capital and the technology plus the market to exploit them. Some of these nations would benefit most not from nuclear power but from a more general program of technical assistance.

Power is important for future generations, but the production of foodstuffs is even more critical as we reckon with the problems of the next century. Each week that passes sees one-quarter million more human beings on our planet. Expert predictions of future populations turn out to be too conservative. The earth's human population has jumped from one billion to its present value in the short span of a single century. It will double again within much less than a century and soon there will be five billion people in the world. This day is uncomfortably close, and the problems associated with this bulging growth are every bit as threatening as the control of the superbomb. The population "bomb" just happens to have a longer fuse.

The upward curve of human production is rising sharply, more precipitously than the sluggish arc of food production. And the empty space between the divergent curves represents abject human misery— hunger, malnutrition, disease and discontent. There are two ways to bridge the gap between the over-abundance of people and the lack of adequate food. One is to restrain the growth of populations; an international control problem more difficult than that for nuclear weapon bans. The other is to boost the production of foodstuffs. Science can most assuredly contribute to a slowdown of the population chain reaction, although the problem transcends the competence of the scientist. And we know from our discussions about atomic agriculture that man's ingenuity can reap more harvest per acre of land and preserve this harvest more efficiently. Nuclear power, moreover, can contribute to public works projects such as irrigation systems, fertilizer production and rural electrification. Further explorations into the mysteries of plant growth, crop nourishment and soil fertility hold great promise for a more abundant future.

However, food production is a problem which may find solution more in political agreements than in scientific developments. The great inequity in national resources between a rich country like the U.S.A. and China for example, cannot be dissipated by the magic wand of science. And we know that richly endowed nations seek to preserve their corpulence. Yet, if men seek the ways of peace and eventuality thrust off the heavy burden of armament and national self-interest, there will be a great wealth of consumer goods available for world markets.

Just the other day I added up the sums which the United States has spent on national defense during the past "peaceful" decade, and I found the brain-numbing total of almost one-third trillion dollars has been spent on armament. The money spent in providing rocket assistance for the take-off of a modern bomber is more than enough to see a youth through four years of college life. Moreover, a great fraction of all scientific research and development concentrates on destruction. Just imagine the pace of science in a world released from the scourge of war!

What I am saying in these few pages amounts to this: humanity quavers before a short-fused super-bomb and a slowly ticking population bomb. The forces of the latter are more distant but are no less potent than the former. I have concerned myself primarily with nuclear explosives because of my own intimacy with these weapons.

All projections of the future tacitly assume that the clock of history will not spin backward in a nuclear cataclysm. Fear of such a catastrophe has haunted scientists from the moment that their senses perceived the pent-up violence of the split atom. That is why a number of atomic scientists—a small and rather lonely group—have repeatedly spoken out about the perils of nuclear warfare. One of the most articulate of this breed of vocal scientists is Dr. Eugene Rabinowitch, editor of the *Bulletin of the Atomic Scientists*. Russian-born Rabinowitch is a rotund, world-renowned chemist who spends most of his time in a basement botany laboratory on the campus of the University of Illinois. Somehow, he finds time, usually in the wee hours of the morning, to edit the *Bulletin* and to fashion editorial messages dedicated to examination of science and its impact upon society. The following sample illustrates the scalpel-like quality of Rabinowitch's pen:

In the long intervals between earthquakes, floods and other elemental catastrophes, the dangers which threaten life are the kind with which human beings can cope. Sometimes man wins over these dangers, and sometimes blind destructive forces win over man, but, in the long run, humanity has been able not only to survive but to assert itself more and more effectively as master of its own fate.

The world in which nuclear forces are on the loose is a world in which man cannot survive by the same kind of endurance, cleverness, and luck which have permitted him to survive in the "chemical" world of yesterday. The rapid advance of scientific thought has projected mankind into an alien world where temperatures are measured in millions of degrees and pressures in millions of atmospheres. Man can survive in this world of incredible violence only by a similarly spectacular progress in social and political wisdom.

Quite a few years have passed since Rabinowitch carved out this editorial; yet there is little evidence for man's coming to grips with his new world. It still remains an alien world. Some scientists have left the sanctity of their ivory towers to preach the gospel of a new world and to warn of the darkness of a nuclear Armageddon. Their house organ, the *Bulletin of the Atomic Scientists,* features a cover design showing two hands of a clock, with only minutes left before midnight. Inside the jacket, on the masthead, is a quotation from Senator Brien McMahon: "It is our solemn obligation, I think, to lift our eyes above the lesser problems that seem to monopolize our time and to discuss and act upon what, by any standard, is the supreme problem before our country and the world." These words were uttered only a few days before Senator McMahon died of cancer.

The scientists have spoken out, exercising what Alexis de Toqueville called "manly candor and masculine independence of opinion," but one wonders if their words have been heard. Many people in the United States do not understand the scientist and view with suspicion or mistrust this breed of man who speaks out so boldly and who thrusts himself into arenas where science has not ventured before. There is a blind tendency to blame the scientist for the bomb and its disruption of the old world power balance. There is deep reluctance to admit that ours is a new world, a place quite different from its preatomic predecessor. Our spinning globe seems the same, diplomats practice their trade, generals plan for war and people persist in their old ways. The new ways of science seem strange and forbidden to trespass by the uninitiate.

To be sure, science is supported in the United States if we reckon assistance on a dollar basis. Somewhat over two billion dollars each year goes for scientific research and development, and this figure will mushroom to ten billion dollars by 1970. But science gets treated like a slot machine that is guaranteed to pay off and spew out results which will be of practical value. J. Robert Oppenheimer, whose candor springs from troubled, deep distress, has incised the issue most acutely. "We know how little of the deep new knowledge which has altered the face of the world, which has changed—and increasingly and ever more, profoundly must change—man's views of the world, resulted from a quest for practical ends or an interest in exercising the power that knowledge gives," the Princeton scientist explained, and then went on in an introspective mood: "For most of us, in most of those moments when we were most free of corruption, it has been the beauty of the world of nature and the strange and compelling harmony of its order, that has sustained, inspirited, and led us."

I know that scientists are often looked upon as cold, dispassionate automatons. Very often, it is implied that they are without religious conviction and are blind seekers of truth. This is partly the fault of the ivory tower residents who seal themselves off from society and fail to communicate to others the joy and beauty of their dedication. Science is now too important a part of society to remain isolated and misunderstood. The national security, both in the usual military sense and in terms of our future welfare, gravitates around a scientific nucleus. Huge laboratories, billions of dollars and a stepped-up production of scientists will not insure our security. We need scientists who can afford to stand aside from the rush of events, who can be immune to pressure for practical results and who can provide the nutritional ideas for the future. Progress in science is measured in units of ideas not in man years or in millions of dollars. When we talk of ideas, we really think of genius, and among the men of genius who have remade the world in which we live none has contributed more than the late Albert Einstein.

It is to this intrepid creator of revolutionary ideas that I turn to end my imperfect description of atoms and people and the way in which they are changing our lives. A few years before he died, Albert Einstein looked out upon the world and its peril to which he had unwittingly contributed. Our century's greatest world-citizen spoke out:

Science has brought forth this danger; but the real problem is in the minds and hearts of men.

We will not change the hearts of other men by mechanism but by changing our hearts and speaking bravely . . .

When we are clear in heart and mind—only then shall we find courage to surmount the fear which haunts the world.

GLOSSARY OF NUCLEAR TERMS

Accelerator A machine which physicists use to produce high energy particles capable of inducing nuclear reactions. A common accelerator is the *cyclotron* which whirls atomic particles around in a circle, using magnetic and electric fields, until they reach an energy measured in millions of volts.

Alamogordo Site in New Mexico of the first experimental A-bomb test on July 16, 1945.

Artificial radioactivity Radioactivity which is induced in any element by exposing it to a beam of nuclear particles such as neutrons. First discovered by Joliot-Curie in 1932. Hundreds of artificial radioactivities have been discovered ranging from radioactive species of hydrogen to radiocobalt and in elements beyond uranium. (See *isotope*.)

Atom Literally "that which is indivisible." The atom is composed of a nucleus and a satellite structure of electrons. There are ninety-two elements, counting those up to uranium, and, in addition, nine more man-made transuranium elements. About one thousand different kinds of atoms (i.e., isotopes) are known to exist.

Atomic bomb A deliberately uncontrolled nuclear chain reaction which converts bomb material into a multimillion-degree hot gas. One pound of bomb stuff is the equal of nine thousand tons of TNT. (See *chain reaction, bomb material*.)

Atomic energy is the name given to energy released in nuclear reactions, originally in uranium. A chain reaction or sequence of splitting of uranium atoms releases energy in the form of heat. In uncontrolled chain reactions the energy comes out in a violent explosion (see *atomic bomb*); in controlled form, the energy is evolved gradually as nuclear power (which see). Atomic energy is derived from the core or nucleus of an atom whereas chemical energy originates in the electron shells outside the nucleus. Nuclear energy is a more correct term for this form of energy which is millions of times more powerful than chemical energy.

Atomic Energy Commission (AEC) An organization established by the Atomic Energy Act of 1946 (McMahon Act) to handle the atomic energy developments in the United States. It is headed by a five-member Commission in Washington, D.C., and it operates production facilities with a total capital investment of $7 billion. Its annual budget is roughly $2 billion. The AEC's Los Alamos Laboratory supervises the development of nuclear weapons and other laboratories (Argonne, Brookhaven and Oak Ridge, Tennessee) do research on applied atomic energy.

Atomic number is the number which uniquely describes any chemical element. Hydrogen, for example, has atomic number 1, iron is 26, gold 79 and uranium is 92. Elements are arranged in order of their atomic number in a periodic system known as the Periodic Table. In addition to an atomic number, there is a *mass number* which describes the different weights for atoms of the same element. (See *isotope.*)

Atomic power See *nuclear power.*

Beryllium, the fourth element in the Periodic Table, is a light metal which is useful in nuclear reactors since it has good physical properties and does not absorb neutrons strongly. Thus we call beryllium a good *moderator* (which see).

Bikini An atoll in the Marshall Islands which is used for the experimental detonation of nuclear weapons. Two bomb tests were conducted there in 1946. A super-bomb was exploded on March 1, 1954, and produced the radioactive fall-out which contaminated the *Lucky Dragon,* a Japanese tuna trawler.

Bomb material Also called *fissionable material* in the case of A-bombs. The basic bomb material is uranium-235 which is separated from natural uranium. Two other materials, uranium-233 and plutonium-239, are derived from thorium and uranium in a nuclear reactor and are also bomb materials, Fissionable material is produced at Oak Ridge, Tennessee; Paducah, Kentucky; and Portsmouth, Ohio, separation plants. Two other AEC sites are at Hanford, Washington, and near Aiken, South Carolina.

Breeder A nuclear reactor which breeds (see below) fissionable material. (See also *power-breeder.*)

Breeding A process whereby fertile material, such as thorium or uranium, is converted into fissionable material inside a nuclear reactor, in such a way that more than one fissionable atom is produced for every atom fissioned in the chain reaction. Breeding allows man to tap the energy of thorium and uranium rather than being restricted to a small fraction of the uranium present in nature. (See *conversion*.)

Chain reaction   A sequence of fissions in a material such as uranium or plutonium in which neutrons released in one generation of fissions cause splitting of other atoms and thus propagate a chain of nuclear reactions (which see). In an atomic bomb the chain reaction may race through eighty generations in less than one millionth of a second.

Control rod   A rod composed of neutron-absorbing material, cadmium, boron or hafnium, which is positioned within a chain reactor in order to control the chain reaction. Pulling the rod out of the reactor starts up the machine and raises the output power. Pushing it in lowers the power and tends to stop the chain reaction.

Conversion   A process whereby a *fertile material* such as thorium or uranium is converted into a *fissionable material*, such as uranium-233 or plutonium-239. This is the technique whereby the huge production plants at Hanford, Washington, and near Aiken, South Carolina, turn out plutonium in high-power nuclear reactors. (See *nuclear reactor*.)

Critical size.   The smallest amount of fissionable material which will just sustain a chain reaction. In the case of an A-bomb, this is about the size of a baseball. No chain reaction can be achieved in a smaller amount of fissionable material.

Curie   A unit of radioactivity, named after Marie and Pierre Curie, which describes the rate at which a substance emits nuclear radiation. One gram ($\frac{1}{28}$ ounce) of radium has an activity of one curie.

Cyclotron   An atom-smasher which accelerates nuclear particles to high energy by whirling them in a circular path inside an intense magnetic field. (See also *accelerator*.)

Deuterium is the name for heavy or double-weight hydrogen and has the symbol D or H^2. There is about one atom of heavy hydrogen for every five thousand atoms of ordinary or light-weight hydrogen (H^1). Combined with oxygen, it forms heavy water (which see).

Electron   The sole constituent of the outer or extranuclear part of the atom. Every atom has orbital electrons which equal in number the value of the atom's atomic number. Electrons are also emitted from hot filaments such as in a vacuum tube or television tube.

Enriched material Ordinary uranium contains only one part of uranium-235 for 140 parts of uranium (which is 99.3 per cent U^{238}). Uranium may be increased or enriched in its percentage of U^{235} by processing it in *separation plants*. Enriched material is valued at $25 per gram of contained U^{235}. Pure fissionable material would thus be over $10,000 per pound.

Fall-out (radioactive) refers to bomb debris which falls from the bomb cloud to the earth's surface, either as visible or invisible dust. Most of the fall-out radioactivity is due to split atoms of uranium. (See *fission products*.) Fall-out occurs locally where bombs are tested close to the earth's surface. Global fall-out takes place when the bomb cloud circles the earth.

Fertile material Either uranium or thorium which is placed inside the core of a nuclear reactor or around it, so that neutrons convert it into fissionable material. (See *conversion*.)

Fission (nuclear) A nuclear reaction in which a heavy atom splits into two parts. We generally think of fission as the phenomenon associated with uranium bombarded with neutrons. The fission of uranium produces a large amount of energy which appears in the form of heat. (See *nuclear reactor, chain reaction*.)

Fissionable material Primarily, uranium-235; but we also include plutonium-239 and uranium-233 as fissionable material. By "fissionable" we imply that fission takes place in a chain reaction produced by neutrons released in fission. Fissionable materials are useful in the production of nuclear power.

Fission product The two halves of the split atom. A lump of uranium in which fission takes place may contain three dozen different fission product elements and two hundred different radioactivities. Almost all fission products are highly radioactive; some remain so for many years.

Fuel rod A rod containing fissionable material which is placed in groups within the core of a nuclear reactor. After prolonged running of the machine, the burn-up of fissionable material in the rod makes it necessary to discharge the rod and replace it.

Fusion The nuclear reaction which describes the sticking together of two light nuclei to form a single more massive nucleus. Since this may be accomplished with heat, as in our sun or in a superbomb, it is often called a *thermonuclear reaction*. A common fusion is that of two atoms of hydrogen to form a single atom of helium. (See *thermonuclear reaction, hydrogen bomb, superbomb*.)

Gamma ray A highly penetrating radiation like X rays which is emitted from radioactive materials. It is best absorbed with heavy elements such as lead although concrete may be used, too. Gamma rays form a radiation hazard associated with atomic explosions, fall-out and nuclear reactors.

Geiger counter An electronic gadget which is widely used to detect and measure radioactivity. It is an exceedingly sensitive device which may respond to the passage through it of a single nuclear particle. Electronic circuits are used to amplify the discharge in the Geiger counter (often called Geiger-Mueller counter) and record it as a flash of light in a neon bulb, a click in an earphone or as a deflection of an instrument needle on a dial. Such counters are useful in prospecting for uranium.

H-bomb or Hydrogen bomb. See *superbomb*.

Half-life A term scientists use to describe the radioactivity of a given material. It is the time required for a substance to decay to one half of its original radioactivity. Radium, for example, has a half life of 1,600 years; U^{238}—4.5 billion years; carbon-14 has 5,600 years and strontium-90 is 28 years. Half-lives may be much shorter, even less than a tiny fraction of a second.

Heavy hydrogen See *deuterium*.

Heavy water Ordinary water is composed of molecules having two atoms of light hydrogen combined with an atom of oxygen (i.e., H_2O). However, some molecules of water contain the rare heavy form of hydrogen (deuterium); on an average there is one atom of heavy hydrogen for every five thousand atoms of the light hydrogen. Heavy water, i.e., that containing heavy hydrogen, can be separated from ordinary water and costs $28 per pound. It is useful as a moderator in nuclear reactors (which see).

Hydrogen power When two atoms of hydrogen fuse to form a single atom of helium, energy is released; this is known as hydrogen energy. Research is under way to find some way of harnessing this H-power for the production of electricity. It is expected that a decade or more will be required to find the means of controlling this fusion energy. (See *fusion*.)

Implosion A term used to describe the inward focusing of high explosives in triggering an A-bomb. Large lens-shaped pieces of TNT form a sphere which is wired so that all segments explode simultaneously. The resulting explosion produces a blast wave, part of which is directed inward and crushes the inner "nuke" into a critical assembly. (See *"nuke"*, *critical size*.)

Isotope   If a pure chemical element such as tin is examined with a delicate weighing device which can sort out atoms of different weight, it is found that tin has ten different weight atoms or isotopes. Some elements like gold, phosphorus, tantalum and iodine have only a single isotope, but most other elements have two or more. (See *radioisotope*, *mass number*.)

Joint Committee on Atomic Energy   A special committee of Congress composed of nine Senators and nine Representatives, given the responsibility of monitoring the decisions and operations of the Atomic Energy Commission.

Kiloton   is a term used to measure the explosive power of a nuclear weapon. It is abbreviated kt and stands for the equivalent of one thousand tons of TNT. Often used to measure the power of A-bombs.

Manhattan Project   The code name for the wartime atomic energy project in the United States, administered by the Manhattan Engineer District of the War Department and headed up by General L. R. Groves. Its facilities were taken over by the Atomic Energy Commission as of January 1, 1947.

Mass-energy relation   Einstein's famous $E = mc^2$ equation which relates mass and energy. Formulated in 1905, this equation is basic to all atomic energy and nuclear physics. According to Einstein's relation, a tiny amount of mass (m), if it can be transformed in a reaction, is equivalent to a vast amount of energy (E); the multiplier c^2 being the square of the velocity of light. On this basis a pound of uranium has an energy equivalent of ten million tons of TNT. However, the energy released in the fission of one pound of uranium amounts to only nine thousand tons of TNT or one-tenth of 1 per cent of the total energy.

Mass number   The number which designates the weight of any isotope and is written as a superscript to the chemical symbol; for example, U^{235}. Hydrogen has three isotopes and thus three mass numbers. (See *isotope*.)

Megaton   is the unit used to describe the power of a superbomb. It is the equivalent of one million tons of TNT and is often written as Mt.

Metallurgical Laboratory   Code name for the Chicago laboratory of the Manhattan Project. It is now the Argonne National Laboratory.

Moderator   A light element used in a nuclear reactor to reduce the speed of the fission neutrons. Heavy water, graphite, beryllium and ordinary water are all commonly used moderators; they are distinguished by the ability to slow down the neutrons without removing them from the chain reaction. (See *chain reaction.*)

Neptunium is element 93 produced by adding a neutron to uranium. The most important isotope of neptunium is Np^{239} produced by the capture of fission neutrons in U^{238}. Np^{239} decays quickly to form long-lived plutonium (Pu^{239}), which see.

Neutron   A fundamental building block of all matter, discovered by Sir James Chadwick in 1932. Neutrons produce (fission in uranium and are also produced) when the uranium atom splits. Such fission neutrons are responsible for the production of the chain reaction.

Nuclear power   Also known as atomic power, it is the electrical power produced from heat released in a chain reaction. A nuclear reactor substitutes for the firebox of a conventional steam-electric plant. (See *nuclear reactor, uranium.*)

Nucleus   The heart or core of an atom. It contains 99.9 per cent of the total mass of the atom and is the source of nuclear energy. It is a tiny, hard kernel which can be disrupted by the impact of neutrons or high-speed nuclear particles.

"Nuke"   The nickname given to the active core of a nuclear weapon.

Periodic Table   An orderly arrangement of all elements according to their chemical similarity. Elements are arranged in order of atomic number in rows and columns. One column, for example, contains all inert gases: helium, neon, argon, krypton, xenon, etc.

Pile   The early name given to a *nuclear reactor.*

Pitchblende   A mineral form containing uranium compounds. Extensive deposits of high-grade pitchblende are found in the Belgian Congo and also in Canada.

Plutonium   The element having atomic number 94 which is produced in a chain reactor. It is the descendent of neptunium-239 and is a fissionable material useful in an A-bomb.

Plutonium-239 has a half-life of 24,000 years. (See *transuranium elements.*)

Radioactivity is the phenomenon of instability of certain nuclei and is characterized by the emission of nuclear particles or gamma rays. Each radioactive substance has its own specific decay rate or *half-life.* (See *artificial radioactivity.*)

Radiocarbon Specifically carbon-14, it is a long-lived radioactive form of element number 6 (carbon). It has a half-life of 5,600 years and is formed in small amounts in nature. Carbon-14 may also be manufactured in a nuclear reactor and may be used as a tracer.

Radioisotope is the name given to a radioactive isotope. Hundreds of such radioisotopes have been produced artificially and many have found valuable use in biology, medicine, agriculture and industry.

Roentgen (unit) is the unit used to measure the absorption of penetrating nuclear radiation. Originally applied to X rays, the r-unit is now applied to other radiation as well. The lethal dose of radiation for a human is about 400 roentgens or 400 r. The maximum permissible dose for atomic workers is 0.3 r per week.

Separation plants are the huge Oak Ridge type plants designed to separate U^{235} from natural uranium. The gaseous diffusion type plant built at Oak Ridge, Tennessee, during the war cost $550 million. Other diffusion plants have been built at the AEC sites near Paducah, Kentucky, and Portsmouth, Ohio. (See *enriched material.*)

Shielding is absorbing material placed between a source of radiation and a person to be protected from the dangerous rays. In the case of a radioactive material emitting gamma (X rays) rays, the best shielding is a heavy element such as lead. Nuclear reactors also emit neutrons and this calls for a light element as the best shield; concrete is often used as a compromise shielding material to absorb both neutrons and gamma rays.

Strontium or element number 38 has a radioisotope (strontium-90) which is produced in fission and has a half-life of 28 years. It is the most toxic poison produced in fission and is a dangerous constituent of radioactive fall-out.

Superbomb or the so-called hydrogen bomb is a nuclear weapon whose power is measured in the millions of tons of TNT (i.e., megatons). It is a three-stage bomb. Stage I consists of an A-bomb trigger. Stage II is a hydrogen-phase involving lithium deuteride as the active material. Stage III involves the fast fission of ordinary uranium.

Thermonuclear reaction is a nuclear reaction in which the initiating particle gains its energy from its thermal motion (heat); also known as fusion (which see). Such reactions with hydrogen account for the evolution of the sun's energy and also that in most of the stars. (See *superbomb.*)

Thorium is element number 90 and has a single isotope of mass number 232 (i.e., Th^{232}). This is a fertile material which is transformed into U^{233}, a fissionable material, by capture of a fission neutron in a nuclear reactor. (See *fertile material.*)

Tritium is a rare, radioactive form of hydrogen; also called triple-weight hydrogen (T or H^3). It can be produced by neutron irradiation of lithium. Titium is useful in the thermonuclear reactions and has a half-life of 12 years.

Transuranium elements are those which are beyond uranium in the Periodic Table, i.e., all have atomic numbers greater than 92. Elements produced and identified to date are: neptunium (93); plutonium (94); americium (95); curium (96); berkelium (97); californium (98); einsteinium (99); fermium (100) and mendelevium (101).

Uranium or element 92 is the key substance of atomic energy. Composed of 99.3 per cent U^{238} and 0.7 per cent U^{235} (with a very small amount of U^{234}) it is a much sought-after metal. Current price for the silvery white metal is $18 per pound. A single pound of uranium is the equal of 2,300,000 pounds of coal or a quarter million gallons of gasoline. (See *fissionable* and *enriched material.*)

X rays are highly penetrating rays discovered by Dr. Roentgen in 1895. X rays are easily produced in modern X-ray tubes and are widely used in medical diagnosis and therapy. They have exactly the same properties as gamma rays of the same energy.

Zirconium (element number 40) is a metal having low neutron absorption which has become popular as a construction material for the cores of nuclear reactors and for cladding fuel rods. It is used in the U.S.S. *Nautilus,* the first nuclear submarine.

INDEX